Adam F

SPLAT

the → FAKE ←

FACT

Some FAKE FACTS have escaped into the world! How will you STOP THEM?

Doodle on them!

Lasso them!

Laser beam them!

Illustrated by Gemma Correll

BLOOMSBURY
CHILDREN'S BOOKS

LONDON   OXFORD   NEW YORK   NEW DELHI   SYDNEY

BLOOMSBURY CHILDREN'S BOOKS
Bloomsbury Publishing Plc
50 Bedford Square, London, WC1B 3DP, UK

BLOOMSBURY, BLOOMSBURY CHILDREN'S BOOKS and the Diana logo are
trademarks of Bloomsbury Publishing Plc

First published in Great Britain 2018 by Bloomsbury Publishing Plc

A catalogue record for this book is available from the British Library

ISBN: 978 1 4088 8950 3

2 4 6 8 10 9 7 5 3

Printed and bound in Great Britain by CPI Group (UK) Ltd, Croydon CR0 4YY

To find out more about our authors and books visit
www.bloomsbury.com and sign up for our newsletters

DISASTER! CHAOS! CALAMITY!

Dozens of **BAD FACTS** have escaped from **MY IMAGINATION** and (INVADED) this book. Can you spot them and **DESTROY** them?

Write your name here

Thanks — — — — — — — — — — — — —

Cross them out, rip them up, scribble on them, draw SILLY HATS on them, whatever it takes to turn this book back into a **NORMAL FACT BOOK** - free from **PIFFLE** and (TWADDLE.)

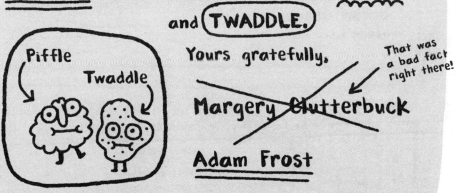

Piffle

Twaddle

Yours gratefully,

That was a bad fact right there!

Margery ~~Clutterbuck~~

Adam Frost

BARMY BEASTS

One of these animals is IMAGINARY and must be STOPPED before it convinces people it's REAL. But which one?

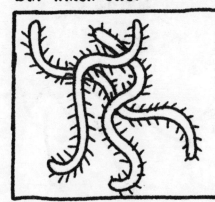

The BONE-EATING ZOMBIE WORM crawls around on the seabed, eating dead whales.

PRINCE AXEL'S WONDER FISH has huge teeth and a luminous fork-shaped organ growing in its mouth.

The SCREAMING HAIRY ARMADILLO screams if you touch it. And it's hairy. And... er... it's an armadillo.

The **MUSICAL FURRY LOBSTER** sings loudly to scare off predators. It's 30 centimetres long and lives in the South Pacific.

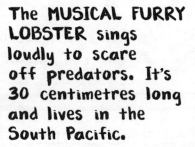

Draw glasses and a ridiculous wig on the impostor.

The **JAVANESE TREE SHEEP** spends most of its life in banyan trees, nibbling leaves and figs.

The **RASPBERRY CRAZY ANT** sometimes eats through cables and electrocutes itself. Crazy!

Which is the MADE-UP monster?

That was a Javanese tree sheep.

SPLAT!

No REAL animals were harmed in the making of this page. And all the other animals are real!

6

DAFT DESTINATIONS

Five of these places are real, but one is TOTALLY MADE-UP. But which one? Scribble on the fake place!

POOPOO

MIDDLEFART

SCRATCHY BOTTOM

VOMIT

ROTTENEGG

MY LARGE INTESTINE

ANSWER
→
Next Page

7

The real places are...

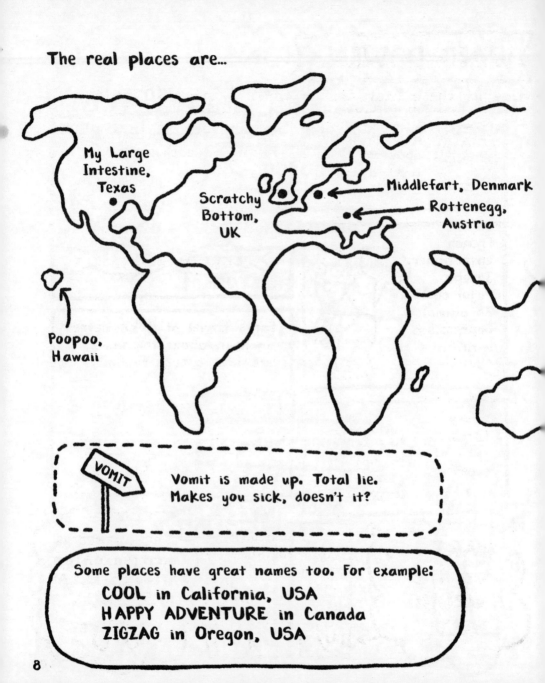

My Large
Intestine,
Texas

Scratchy
Bottom,
UK

Middlefart, Denmark

Rottenegg,
Austria

Poopoo,
Hawaii

VOMIT
Vomit is made up. Total lie.
Makes you sick, doesn't it?

Some places have great names too. For example:
COOL in California, USA
HAPPY ADVENTURE in Canada
ZIGZAG in Oregon, USA

WIND POWER

One of these facts about farts is pure **HOT AIR**.

 Humans fart about 14 times a day.

Herrings communicate by farting at each other.

Did you say something?

No. Just indigestion.

French entertainer Joseph Pujol could do animal impressions with his farts.

Quack!

Farts travel at 11 kilometres an hour, about the same speed as a child running.

Mouse farts smell of cheese.

Aah!

FART on the WRONG FACT!

Boys and girls fart the same amount.

The answer is written on an **INTERSTELLAR GAS CLOUD.**

OUT OF THIS WORLD

When scientists discover a new planet, they give it a name. But which of these is a PRETEND PLANET?

Elvis

Einstein

Roger
Federer

Pocahontas

ANSWER:
Mouse farts
don't smell of
cheese. In fact,
mice don't even
like cheese that
much.

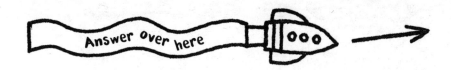
Answer over here

O
Pinocchio

O Glasgow

✦

O Hagrid

O

Asterix

O

Mr Spock

O

🪐

O

Donald Duck

O

O

O

O

Draw a laser beam coming out of this
DEATH RAY. Blow up the FAKE PLANET!

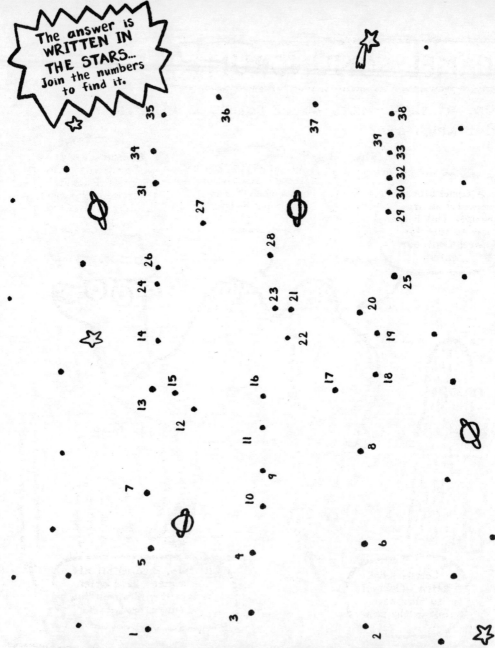

The answer is WRITTEN IN THE STARS... Join the numbers to find it.

All the others are real names given to actual planets.
(If you're stuck, the answer is also on page 155.)

12

CAMEL CONUNDRUM

One of these facts about camels is CLAPTRAP.
But which one?

In the 1970s, a scientist discovered a camel in Yemen with four humps.

The town of San Dimas, USA, has a deputy sheriff called Bert. Bert is a camel.

A camel stores water in its humps. This helps it to last for weeks without water.

Camels have extra wide feet so they don't sink in the sand.

In 2016, a camel bit off its owner's head after he left it tied up all day during a heatwave.

Which fact is the phoney?

MAD MONARCHS

There have been a lot of kings and queens in history. But which one of these rulers isn't real?

Caligula was a Roman emperor who declared war on the sea. He ordered his soldiers to slash at the waves with their swords and collect shells as 'trophies of war'.

← Off with his head?

Is this a made-up monarch?

Charles VI of France believed he was made of glass and wore iron rods in his clothes to stop himself shattering.

I'm cracking up!

After having a nightmare about a lion attacking him, King Farouk of Egypt went to Cairo Zoo and shot all the lions.

Is this a genuine king?

Answer: Camels store fat in their humps, not water.

King Gustav of Saxony believed he could lay eggs like a bird. He had a special throne made with a nest on it.

An unreal ruler?

Princess Alexandra of Bavaria believed she'd swallowed a grand piano made of glass as a girl – which was still inside her.

True or tripe?

Eric XIV of Sweden had people executed if they laughed in his presence. He also spent long periods believing he was his own brother.

False or fact?

Ferdinand I of Austria rarely talked. One of the only things anyone ever heard him say was: 'I am the emperor and I want dumplings'.

Fact or fiction?

Which **IMPOSTOR** will end up **IN THE STOCKS?**

KILLER CREATURES

Here are eight deadly animals. And one animal that's NEVER killed a human.

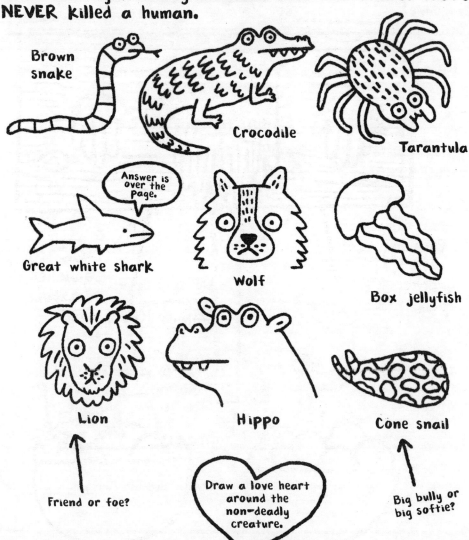

Brown snake

Crocodile

Tarantula

Answer is over the page.

Great white shark

Wolf

Box jellyfish

Lion

Hippo

Cone snail

Friend or foe?

Draw a love heart around the non-deadly creature.

Big bully or big softie?

How many people does each animal kill every year (on average)?

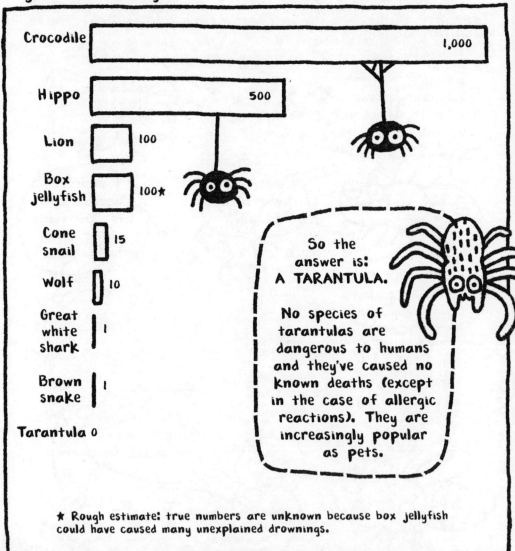

Crocodile — 1,000

Hippo — 500

Lion — 100

Box jellyfish — 100★

Cone snail — 15

Wolf — 10

Great white shark — 1

Brown snake — 1

Tarantula — 0

So the answer is: **A TARANTULA.**

No species of tarantulas are dangerous to humans and they've caused no known deaths (except in the case of allergic reactions). They are increasingly popular as pets.

★ Rough estimate: true numbers are unknown because box jellyfish could have caused many unexplained drownings.

BAD BUGS

One of these insect facts is a fib and must be SQUISHED. But which one?

Fold the page along this line to find the answer.

Earwigs lay eggs in your ears.

For every person on Earth, there are 200 million insects.

Woodlice have blue blood.

Rhinoceros beetles can lift 850 times their own bodyweight.

Fleas can jump 80 times their own height.

Only female wasps can sting you.

And only female mosquitoes drink your blood.

Which bug is bluffing?

That was the earwig. SQUELCH!

FANTASTICAL BEASTS

Some prehistoric animals were EPIC. But which one of these is a monster myth?

Archaeoraptor was a small flying dinosaur with wings and feathers – like a turkey with teeth.

Yutyrannus was like a T. rex but with bright and fluffy feathers. Pretty Polly!

Tanystropheus had a three metre body and a three metre neck, like a snake attached to a crocodile's body.

This is the asteroid that wiped out the dinosaurs. Draw it in the sky, heading for the DODGY DINO.

Quetzalcoatlus was a pterosaur with a wingspan of 11 metres, over three times wider than any bird alive today.

Surreal or NOT real?

Answer this way →

Helicoprion was a shark with a whirl of teeth in its mouth – like a circular saw.

Opabinia was a sea creature with two rows of legs, five eyes on stalks and a hoover-like trunk with a claw on the end.

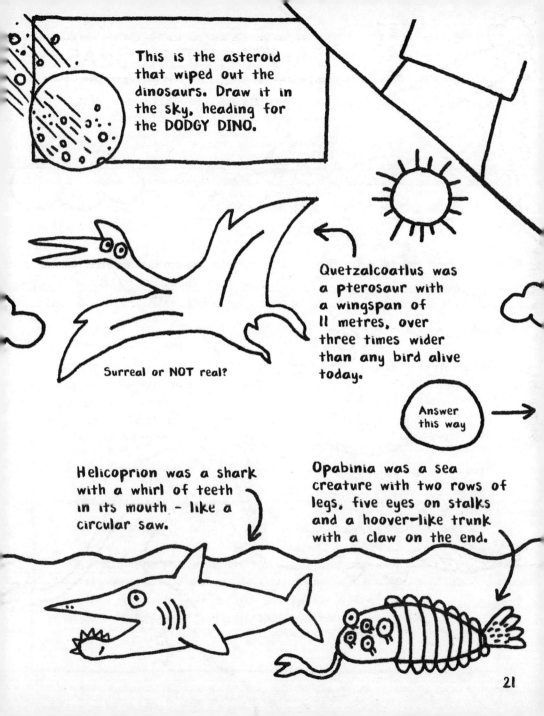

Yutyrannus, Tanystropheus, Opabinia, Helicoprion and Quetzalcoatlus were all REAL.

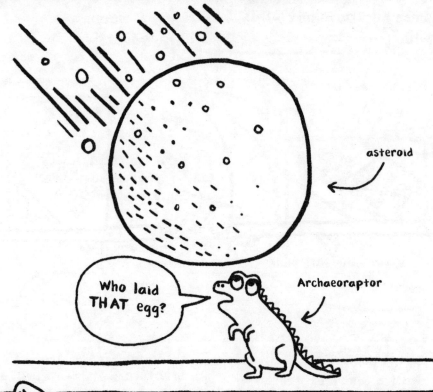

asteroid

Who laid THAT egg?

Archaeoraptor

Archaeoraptor was a dino-sized HOAX! In 1999, a farmer from China stuck a bird's head and body on to a dinosaur's bottom – then tried to sell it for a fortune. It fooled scientists for a few months, but on closer inspection they realised it was a fiendish forgery!

NONSENSE NAMES

If you travel abroad, some things in the supermarket can have **VERY STRANGE** names. But which of these is a **PRETEND** product?

Must be made up!

PLOPP

ZIT

BARF

BUM BUM

SNOTT

PIPI

Surely a sham!

ANSWER
Snott is made up! Plopp is a Swedish chocolate bar. Zit is a Greek soft drink. Bum Bum is a German ice cream. Pipi is a Croatian soft drink and Barf is an Iranian washing powder.

EGYPTIAN FICTION?

So you're an Egyptian pharaoh and it's time to be mummified. Which of these facts about mummification is made up?

1. Your brain is pulled out of your nose with big hooks.

2. Your eyes are replaced with stones or small onions.

It'll end in tears...

3. All your internal organs are removed except your heart.

This is because Egyptians believed that you thought with your HEART (not your brain).

4. You are dressed in a special pair of 'lucky' underpants.

They have your name in hieroglyphics on the front.

5. You're wrapped in about 372 square metres of bandages.

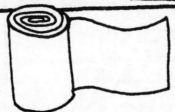

Mummy's bandages: 372 m²

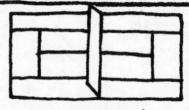

Tennis court: 261 m²

6. You're surrounded by everything you'll need in the afterlife, including...

food

mummified pets

a toilet

7. Sometimes you're surrounded by your servants too.

Worst boss ever

King Djer had over 500 of his servants bumped off and buried with him.

8. Your body would probably be stolen. Every pyramid we know about has been raided at least once.

I'm dead confused.

9. You could be ground down into medicine. In the Middle Ages, people believed that powdered mummy could cure anything.

I want my mummy!

It's coming dear!

10. Meanwhile, your soul would journey to the afterlife. Your soul would be weighed to find out how good you'd been...

Ammit the Devourer

If you'd been naughty, your soul would be eaten by a monster with a crocodile's head and a hippo's bottom.

So which of these facts is FALSE?

The answer is written on the wall of this tomb:

Use this hieroglyphic alphabet to help you:

=A =B =C =D =E

=F =G =H =I =J

=K =L =M =N =O

=P =Q =R =S =T

=U =V =W =X =Y

=Z =CH =KN =SH

When the same symbol is used for TWO DIFFERENT LETTERS, try BOTH and see which makes the most sense. (If you're really stuck, turn to page 155.)

WHAT A BLAST!

Some animals splat themselves. Which of these animals is **NOT** a super splatterer?

BANG!

SPLAT!

Globitermes sulphureus termites explode in a mess of sticky yellow liquid when weaver ants attack their nests.

Carpenter ants blow their heads up when their nests are threatened. This covers the predators in poisonous glue and saves their colonies.

A horned lizard will squirt blood up to 1.5 metres OUT OF ITS EYES when it's attacked. It can use up to a third of its total blood supply splattering intruders.

SQUIRT!

OUCH!

SMASH!

When glass snakes are attacked, their tail shatters into several pieces. These pieces of tail jump around, distracting the predator while the rest of the snake escapes.

Porcupines shoot their spines at other animals when they're cornered. They can fire off half their quills at once, leaving them with bald bottoms!

Answer over here

KIDS' STUFF

Some kids make history. But some kids MAKE STUFF UP. Which of these children is a record-breaking FIBBER?

At the age of 13, Jordan Romero reached the top of Mount Everest, the world's biggest mountain. He also climbed Mount Kilimanjaro - Africa's highest mountain - at the age of ten.

This is the high point of my life.

Kristoffer Von Hassel is the youngest ever hacker. At the age of five, he hacked the Xbox Live password system, gaining access to dozens of free games.

Achievement unlocked!

This report will blow you away!

Jane Haubrich became a TV reporter at the age of five. She reported on a hurricane in Pennsylvania, USA.

I'm looking sharp!

Answer: Porcupines can't 'shoot' their quills. The spikes come off quite easily when the porcupine is attacked and all 30,000 quills are VERY sharp and VERY painful, but they can't be fired like arrows.

At the age of 14, Eloise Drennan became the youngest ever astronaut, visiting the International Space Station for six days.

Draw the child who's fibbing on the naughty step.

At the age of ten, Dimitrios Loundras won an Olympic medal for gymnastics at the 1896 Games.

At eight years old, Tiger Brewer became the youngest ever 'wing-walker'. In 2009, he balanced on the wing of a biplane flying at 160 kilometres per hour.

ANSWER
Eloise Drennan isn't real. The youngest ever astronaut is Gherman Titov who was 25 when he made it to space. But there are NO age restrictions on becoming an astronaut. Could YOU beat his record?

LEONARDO'S LAB

Leonardo Da Vinci was a famous painter and engineer who lived 500 years ago in Italy. But which of these facts about him is a CRAZY INVENTION?

1. He loved animals so much that he would often buy caged pets in markets just so he could set them free.

2. He painted the most famous picture in the world – the Mona Lisa. Some experts say it took him 22 years to finish. Can you imagine spending 22 years on ONE painting?

3. According to a historian from Leonardo's time, the painter was so strong he could unbend horseshoes with a single hand.

4. He once designed a maze for an Italian cardinal that was so complex that two nuns spent 24 hours lost in it.

5. In 1495, he invented a robot knight that could stand up, sit down, and lift up the visor on its helmet.

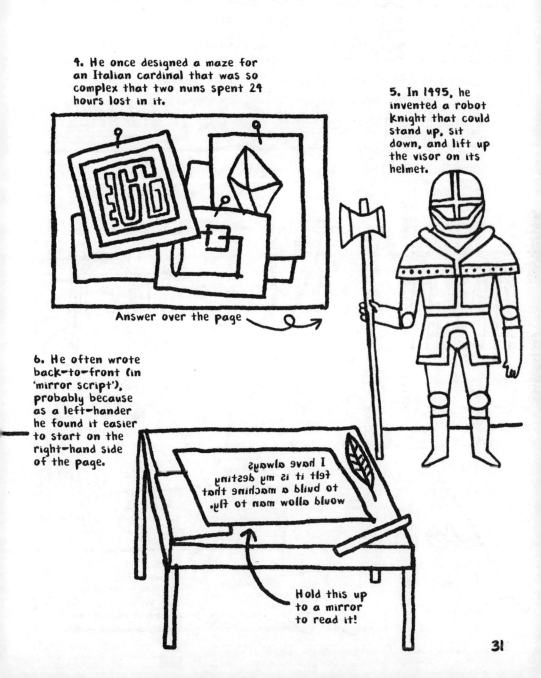

Answer over the page

6. He often wrote back-to-front (in 'mirror script'), probably because as a left-hander he found it easier to start on the right-hand side of the page.

I have always felt it is my destiny to build a machine that would allow man to fly.

Hold this up to a mirror to read it!

Colour in all the 'number 3' areas to find the answer.

(If you're really stuck, turn to page 155 for the answer.)

BARMY BANDS

You've probably heard of the Beatles. Or U2. Or One Direction. But some bands have really nutty names. Which of these barmy bands is MADE-UP?

THE BAND FORMERLY KNOWN AS SAUSAGE

DEAD CABBAGE CAFE

CHOCOLATE BUNNIES FROM HELL

SNOT

HALF MAN HALF BISCUIT

ELECTRIC VOMIT

PEOPLE WITH CHAIRS UP THEIR NOSES

***** THE ENTIRE POPULATION OF CHINA *****

Answer over here

The name of the made-up band is written here in musical notes. If you can't read music, we've put a scale at the bottom of the page.

Write the names of the notes here.

This will spell out the BAD band name.

A B C D E F G

If you're still stuck, turn to page 155 for the answer.

34

LOL!

Here are some of the most common acronyms★ in English. But each one has GOOD and BAD definitions.

Circle the GOOD one!

What does each acronym stand for?

D.O.B.	Don't Offend Badgers	OR	Date of Birth
F.A.Q.	Farts Attack Quickly	OR	Frequently Asked Questions
S.O.S.	Save Our Souls	OR	Seriously Orange Snot
V.I.P.	Very Itchy Pants	OR	Very Important Person
U.S.B.	Universal Serial Bus	OR	Unbelievably Smelly Burp
U.F.O.	Unidentified Flying Object	OR	Unexplained Farting Outbreak

★ **WHAT IS AN ACRONYM?**
An acronym is when you use the first letter of each word in a phrase to make a shorter or easier version.

This way for the answer

DEAD AND BURIED

Some people have come back from the dead – like ZOMBIES. But which of these stories is DEAD untrue?

In 2013, 95-year-old Li Xiufeng hit her head and was pronounced dead. She was placed in an open coffin in her house for a week. The day before she was due to be buried, neighbours found the coffin empty and Li in her kitchen, cooking lunch.

In 2014, 91-year-old Janina Kolkiewicz was believed to be dead. She was zipped up in a body bag and placed in a hospital freezer. Eleven hours later, hospital staff saw her body bag MOVE through the window and quickly whipped her out. She asked for hot tea and pancakes.

Answers: 1. Date of Birth, 2. Frequently Asked Questions, 3. Save Our Souls,

YOU RANG?
In Victorian times, some people asked to be buried in 'safety coffins'. These contained bells that the 'dead person' could ring if they came back to life.

Answer on the next page ——→

In May 2012, the family of Hamdi Hafez al-Nubi were preparing his body for burial. A doctor was brought in to sign his death certificate, but she realised that the man was still breathing. After reviving Mr al-Nubi, she then revived his mother (who had fainted).

In 1915, Essie Dunbar had an epileptic fit and was pronounced dead. Her sister arrived at the funeral late – and asked to see her sister one last time. The coffin was opened and Essie sat up and smiled. She lived for another 47 years.

In 1930, Russian monk Ivan Shufflov was mistakenly buried after eating too much ham at a monastery supper and lapsing into a coma. As his coffin was lowered into the ground, monks heard a loud burp and Ivan demanding his pudding.

ART ATTACK!

There are some strange sculptures in the world. But which one of these do you think is too loopy to be true?

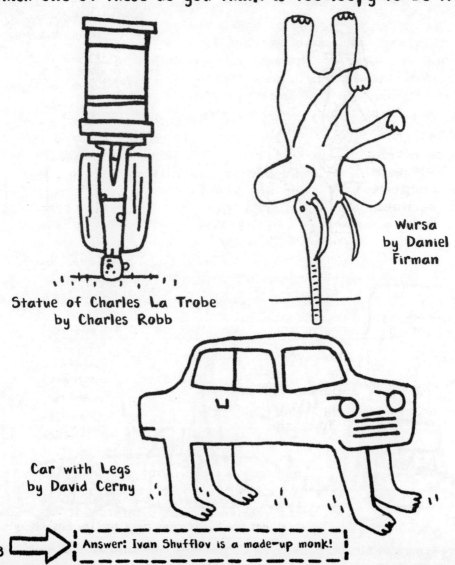

Statue of Charles La Trobe
by Charles Robb

Wursa
by Daniel
Firman

Car with Legs
by David Cerny

Answer: Ivan Shufflov is a made-up monk!

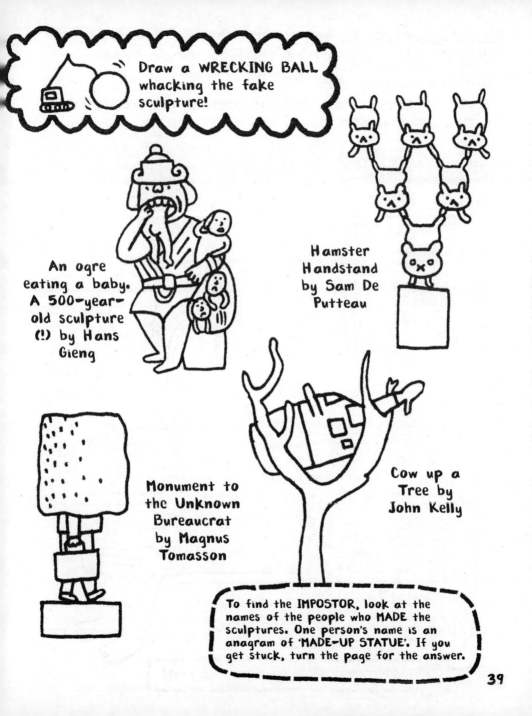

Draw a WRECKING BALL whacking the fake sculpture!

An ogre eating a baby. A 500-year-old sculpture (!) by Hans Gieng

Hamster Handstand by Sam De Putteau

Monument to the Unknown Bureaucrat by Magnus Tomasson

Cow up a Tree by John Kelly

To find the IMPOSTOR, look at the names of the people who MADE the sculptures. One person's name is an anagram of 'MADE-UP STATUE'. If you get stuck, turn the page for the answer.

MIDDLE AGE MAYHEM

Which of these stained-glass scenes of medieval life is **MUMBO JUMBO**? Colour in the **TRUE** facts!

Football was banned in England by King Edward III. In fact, he banned all sport except archery, which people had to practise for two hours every Sunday.

Colour it in if you believe it!

Correct or crazy?

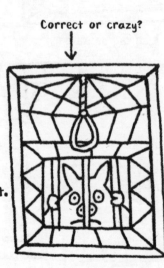

Chickens, moles and locusts were all put on trial in the Middle Ages. In 1386, a pig was found guilty of murder in a French court. It was dressed up as a man and hanged in the town square.

Most medieval Brits believed green vegetables - especially cabbages - were bad for you. Tomatoes, which arrived in the 1500s, were thought to be poisonous too.

Answer: Sam De Putteau

Answer this way! ➡

Medieval monks slept fully clothed and kept their 'braies' (or pants) on when they had a bath.

Most castle moats contained either crocodiles, alligators or BOTH to stop invaders swimming across. Leeds Castle in Kent contained over 100 crocs!

↳ Yay or nay?

Medieval medicine was weird! One popular cure for the plague involved shaving the bottom half of a chicken and then rubbing its bald bottom on your swollen armpits.

A suit of armour could weigh as much as 50 kilograms. That's heavier than you!★ Imagine trying to run, fight or climb on a horse in that! And what if you needed the toilet...?

★ 50 kilograms is the average weight of a 15-year-old child!

Oh no! Someone's kicked a football through the BAD FACT! (Maybe that's why King Edward banned it...) If you cut out the pieces, and rearrange them, you should be able to work out the answer.

(Or if you don't fancy cutting up this lovely book, the answer is on page 156.)

ROBIN'S ROBBERS

Shoot an arrow at the made-up character!

You've heard of Robin Hood and his Merry Men, right? But which of these characters **NEVER** feature in any of the traditional stories?

Is he your target?

FRIAR TUCK
Always jolly, partial to a pie or three.

WILL SCARLET
The youngest of the Merry Men, he likes to wear red.

LITTLE JOHN
Robin's right-hand man. He's not little at all!

SAM THE SAILOR'S SON
Daring and dashing. His favourite phrase is 'I'll save you, Madam!'

Will your arrow end up here?

Mwa ha ha

THE SHERIFF OF NOTTINGHAM
The ultimate baddie. Nobody likes him, but he doesn't care.

ALAN-A-DALE
The resident musician. Handy with a lute (and a flute).

Answer ------> 43

BELIEVE IT OR NOT

Different countries have different superstitions. But which one of these customs have I concocted myself?

1. In the 1930s, yo-yos were banned in Syria, because it was believed they caused drought.

2. In Greece, it is said that if a cat jumps over your grave, you'll come back to life as a vampire.

3. In Denmark, you should throw broken plates at your friend's house on New Year's Eve to wish them good luck. Smashing!

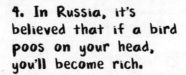

4. In Russia, it's believed that if a bird poos on your head, you'll become rich.

ANSWER
Your arrow should have hit the Sam the Sailor's Son. He's made-up! (Although one of the Merry Men is called Much the Miller's Son.)

5. In China, eating noodles can be MURDER. If you cut a noodle in half, you'll cut your life short too. So slurp them up whole.

6. In Mexico, if you point at a rainbow, you'll get a boil on your nose.

7. In Portugal, limes are unlucky. If you eat food with lime in it, you have to break wind as soon as possible – to fart the bad luck onto someone else.

8. If you live in Argentina and you have six sons, stop right there! A seventh son will become a werewolf.

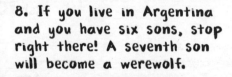

9. In Japan, people give their newborn babies to sumo wrestlers. The babies are then gently shaken until they cry. This is said to bring the baby good health!

Answer ⇨

To find the BAD FACT in our superstition quiz, try 'reading the signs' in this crystal ball...

If you're stuck, turn to page 156.

SNOT TRUE!

Which of these facts about SNOT is ROT?

You swallow about one litre of snot a day or 27,375 litres in a lifetime.

27,375 litres = 5 skips of snot

Ostrich snot used to be regarded as a medicine. Special 'snot doctors' would hold pepper under the birds' beaks to make them sneeze.

Oh no you don't...

Giant larvaceans are tadpoles that live inside huge balls of snot. When something bursts their bogey bubble, they blow a new one.

Donna Griffiths of the UK had the world's longest sneezing fit, sneezing over a million times during a two-and-a-half year period.

Bless you

Bless you

Bless you

Bless you

Bless you

Nottingham in the UK was originally called Snottingham, because it was briefly ruled by a Saxon chieftain called Lord Snot.

No idea why they call me that...

Got to be garbage?

WIPE SNOT ON THE WRONG FACT.

Answer

I've written the answer in snot:

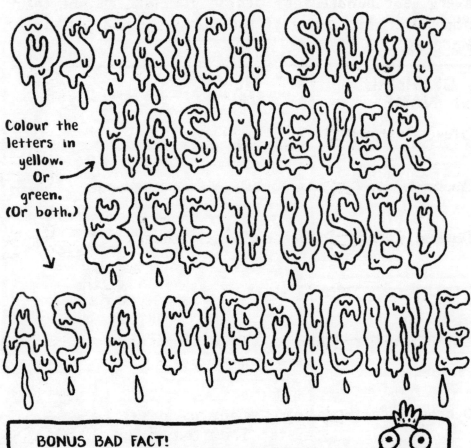

OSTRICH SNOT HAS NEVER BEEN USED AS A MEDICINE

Colour the letters in yellow.
Or green.
(Or both.)

BONUS BAD FACT!
One of the BADDEST facts about ostriches is that they bury their head in the sand when they're scared. They don't! EVER! They either fight (their kick can kill a lion) or run (they can reach 70 kilometres per hour - that's as fast as a greyhound).

NAMING NAMES

Every year hundreds of people officially change their name. Here are some of the wackiest. And ONE I made up.

ORIGINAL NAME		NEW NAME
Steve Boston	⇒	Buzz Lightyear
Simon Smith	⇒	Bacon Double Cheeseburger
Darren Rolph	⇒	Queens Park Rangers
Scott Nall	⇒	Optimus Prime
Colin Spong	⇒	A Wop Bop A Loo Bop A Wop Bam Boom
George Garratt	⇒	Captain Fantastic Faster Than Superman Spiderman Batman Wolverine Hulk And The Flash Combined

ANSWER
Colin Spong didn't change his name to A Wop Bop A Loo Bop A Wop Bam Boom. However, Jeffrey Wilschke DID change his name to Beezow Doo-Doo Zopittybop-bop-bop.

49

THE HIGH LIFE

Hot air balloons are the oldest form of human flight. But which of these facts is a flight of fancy?

In 2010, Christian Brown built a glass-bottomed hot air balloon, meaning that passengers could see the ground HUNDREDS of metres below. Would you give it a try?

In 1808, two Frenchmen, Mr Grandpré and Mr Le Pique, fought a duel in hot air balloons. Mr Grandpré won after shooting a hole in Mr Le Pique's balloon, sending it crashing to the ground.

In 1983, a sheep called Tim accidentally jumped into a hot air balloon in Scotland. It took off, finally crashing into a tree 80 kilometres away. Tim survived unharmed.

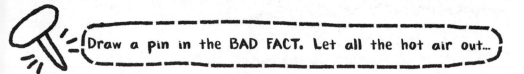

Draw a pin in the BAD FACT. Let all the hot air out...

Colour in the balloon if you think the fact is true! →

One of the first hot air balloons (launched in 1783) was mistaken for a fire-breathing dragon by French peasants. They pulled it to the ground and attacked it with pitchforks.

In 1785, the first balloonists to cross the English Channel noticed their balloon was losing height. They threw their possessions out, then their clothes (except their pants), then finally weed and pooed over the side. It worked! The balloon rose again.

In 2012, Felix Baumgartner flew a giant helium balloon to the edge of space. Then he jumped out, free-falling for over four minutes, reaching a record 1,358 kilometres an hour and BREAKING THE SOUND BARRIER.

Oh no! ALL the balloons have burst! To find out the false fact, you'll have to follow their trails through the sky.

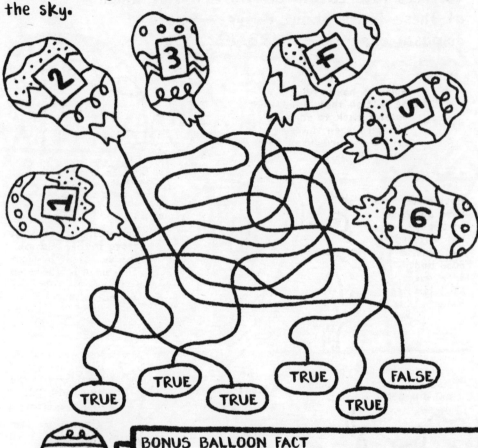

BONUS BALLOON FACT
You might be wondering: how do I steer a hot air balloon? The simple answer is, you don't! However, the wind moves at different speeds at different heights, which gives the pilot SOME control over the balloon's direction.

SUPER SCAVENGERS

Vultures love eating dead stuff. But which of these facts about nature's waste disposal experts is GARBAGE?

Vultures have evolved to be bald so that blood doesn't stick to their feathers when they're rummaging around inside dead animals.

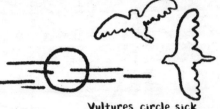

Vultures circle sick animals, waiting for them to die.

Most birds have no sense of smell, but vultures can smell a dead body from over 1.5 kilometres away.

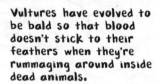

Vultures are often too heavy to fly, because they've eaten so much! They have to throw up if they want to take off again.

Vultures can eat rotten and diseased meat that would kill any other animal.

Vultures wee all over their legs to clean off the blood and kill any bacteria.

Which fact is false? Answer here

ANSWER:
Vultures don't circle sick animals. Most vultures aren't interested in ANYTHING moving. It has to be dead.

53

AHEAD OF HIS TIME

In Tudor England, traitors' heads were put on spikes on London Bridge. Here's an interview with one of those traitors. But **WATCH OUT** – one fact will be a lie.

I'm Ed Choptoff. Or at least I used to be. But how did my ugly mug end up here? Let me give you a heads up.

First, I was sentenced to death. Hundreds of people were executed in Tudor England.

Come on, chop chop!

Crimes that carried the death penalty included...

pickpocketing

stealing food

impersonating an Egyptian★

You could be beheaded like me. But you could also be...

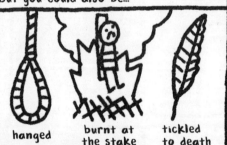

hanged

burnt at the stake

tickled to death

My beheading went smoothly. One chop and it was all over. Others haven't been so lucky...

Mary Queen of Scots	𝔊𝔊𝔊	3 CHOPS
James, Duke of Monmouth	𝔊𝔊𝔊𝔊𝔊	5 CHOPS
Margaret Pole	𝔊𝔊𝔊𝔊𝔊𝔊𝔊𝔊𝔊𝔊𝔊	11 chops (Ouch!)

★ 'Egyptian' was the Tudor word for 'gypsy'

55

I'm Queen Elizabeth I and I've had enough of this **TOMFOOLERY**. I've never read such CODSWALLOP . Why, on the last page, one of my (former) subjects claimed that criminals in Tudor England were TICKLED to death. The very idea! Breaking the law is no laughing matter. I admit that everything else that Mr Choptoff said is **TRUE**. But that's hardly the point. The point is, the only thing that will stop me **CUTTING OFF THE HEADS** of everyone who has ever read this book is if you **GET ME A NEW PUPPY.** Or at least draw a really cuddly one **HERE.**

VOLCANO ZONE

Which of these facts about volcanoes deserves to go up in smoke?

1. There are about 20 volcanoes erupting right now. Three quarters of them are erupting under the sea.

 2. Volcanoes can appear from nowhere. One day in February 1943, the Paricutin volcano surged up in the middle of a field in Mexico. Within a year, it was 336 metres tall.

3. Volcanic bombs are rocks that shoot through the air when volcanoes erupt. In 1935, a volcano in Japan threw a 'bomb' with a six-metre diameter up to 500 METRES through the air.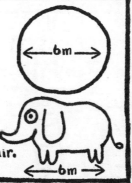

 4. It is impossible to predict when volcanoes are going to erupt.

 5. Thrill seeker alert! A company in Chile allows you to bungee jump into an active volcano. You leap out of a helicopter into the crater, coming to a stop around 200 metres from the red-hot magma below.

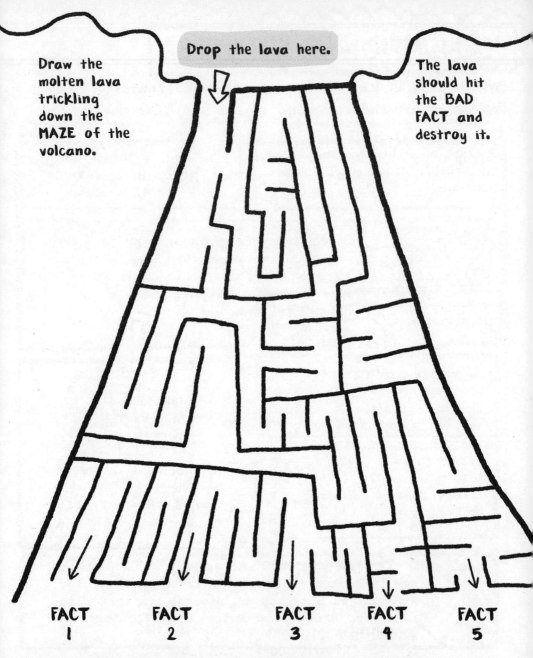

Draw the molten lava trickling down the MAZE of the volcano.

Drop the lava here.

The lava should hit the BAD FACT and destroy it.

FACT 1

FACT 2

FACT 3

FACT 4

FACT 5

Turn to page 156 for more information about the bad fact.

SENSATIONAL STUNTS

Brad Byers is known for his INSANE stunts. But which of the following is a claim TOO FAR?

Too bonkers to be true? ↓

He laid on a bed of nails while his brother drove a quad bike over him.

He swallowed 12 swords at once and twisted them 180° in his mouth.

He released 12 rat traps on his tongue.

Rats!

He broke 46 toilet seats with his head in a minute.

He balanced a (running) lawnmower on his chin for over three minutes.

Answer over here ↘

DON'T TRY THIS AT HOME! Any one of these SHOCKING stunts could kill you!

SURREAL SPORTS

Take a look at these strange sports. Can you guess which one is MADE-UP?

ARMPIT FARTING
This is part of the annual Redneck Games in Georgia, USA. Winners must fart out a famous song – in tune if possible!

TOILET RACING
Every year, in Michigan, USA, dozens of people push around toilets on skis as fast as they can. (All toilets must also have toilet roll dispensers.)

Is this some kind of game?

THE BIG CAKE HIKE
Every June, the Big Cake Hike is held in Virginia, USA. Runners have to cross rivers and jump fences while carrying a huge wedding cake. If the little bride and groom figures on the top fall off, you're out!

Who cooked that up?

ANSWER
Brad Byers didn't break 46 toilet seats with his head in a minute. But Kevin Shelley from the USA did!

YOU'RE OFF!
Do you have a whistle? Blow it loudly at the BAD FACT. Hold up a red card if you've got one. Send the bad fact off!

WORM CHARMING
This event takes place in Willaston, UK. Contestants must 'charm' worms out of the ground by thumping, prodding and playing music. The world record was set in 2009 when a ten-year-old girl caught 567 worms in 30 minutes.

WIFE CARRYING
In this Finnish sport, contestants must carry their wives over a range of obstacles. The winner gets his wife's weight in beer.

GIANT PUMPKIN RACING
Every year in Oregon, USA, hundreds of people race huge hollowed-out pumpkins across a lake. The event also features pumpkin bowling.

I took a dive.

GRAVY WRESTLING
The championships take place each year in Lancashire, UK. 1,000 litres of gravy are poured into a paddling pool. The most entertaining wrestler wins.

Answer

These 11 football players know what the BAD FACT is. They're telling you the answer in a secret code, using the numbers on their shirts.

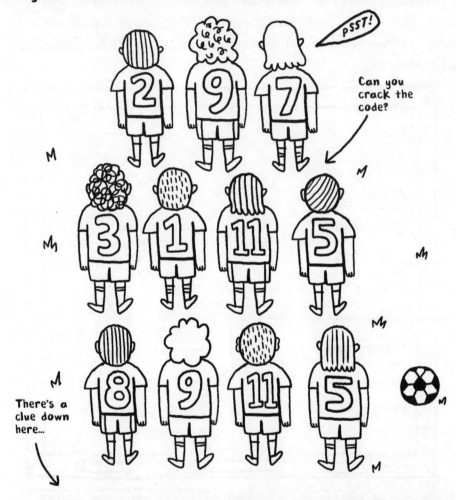

PSST!

Can you crack the code?

There's a clue down here...

Each number here stands for a letter of the alphabet. Why not try substituting 1 for A, 2 for B, 3 for C and so on. What does it spell? Turn to page 156 if you get stuck.

BACKWARDS WORDS

A palindrome is a word or phrase that reads the same forwards and backwards. Use your spelling skills to work out which of these is a PRETEND palindrome?

eye

noon

deed

redivider

desserts

Was it a rat I saw?

Step on no pets.

Never odd or even

Madam, I'm Adam.

Was it a bar or a bat I saw?

kayak

level

poop

radar

racecar

ANSWER

LONDON LIFE

London is the capital of the UK and home to over eight million people. But which of these London facts is fiction?

The London metro is called the Underground, but most of it is overground.

55% overground

45% underground

The strangest things people have left behind on a London tube train include:

a drum kit

a garden slide

a park bench

a stuffed eagle

a grandfather clock

a coffin

Weird.

The world's first traffic light was put up in London in 1868.

Welcome to Earth!

Please don't vaporise us.

The following year, it exploded.

Total twaddle?

The Great Fire of London in 1666 was so fierce that 70,000 of London's 80,000 houses were destroyed.

However, according to official records, only six people died.

In 1647, Christmas and Easter were banned by the Houses of Parliament. This is because the ruling Puritan party thought they were wasteful and unholy.

All shops had to stay open during Easter and Christmas.

Between 1323 and 1325, all male babies in London were given the middle name 'Colin'. This was because the Lord Mayor, Colin Pontefract, wanted every man in London to bear his name.

He's a nightmare Mayor.

COLIN

A likely story?

In 1949, a flock of starlings landed on one of Big Ben's minute hands, causing it to stop for four-and-a-half minutes.

This is cuckoo!

Answer over here

65

To help work out the answer, we've brought in London expert, Cockney Kev. You might need to use the Cockney Rhyming Slang phrasebook over **THERE** to work out what he's saying:

Oi, oi! Could I have a dicky bird, me old china? You see, one of the facts on the last page is a pork pie. If you use your loaf, you can probably figure it out. If you can't, slip me a Lady Godiva and I'll tell yer. Only having a giraffe – no need to give me any bread. So you know that fact about the Mayor calling everyone Colin, well, don't you Adam and Eve it. All the other facts are true, but you never got in Barney Rubble if you didn't call your bin lids Colin.

66

Adam and Eve = believe

apples and pears = stairs

Barney Rubble = trouble

bin lid = kid

bread and honey (or 'bread') = money

butcher's hook = look

china plate (or 'china') = mate

dicky bird = word

giraffe = laugh

Lady Godiva = fiver (five pound note)

loaf of bread (or 'loaf') = head

plates of meat = feet

pork pie = lie

raspberry tart (or raspberry) = fart

Still stumped? Turn to page 157.

Cockney Rhyming Slang was first used in the 1840s in the Seven Dials area of London. It allowed shopkeepers to talk amongst themselves without customers understanding what they were saying. **67**

TECH TALK

One of these facts about technology should be DELETED!

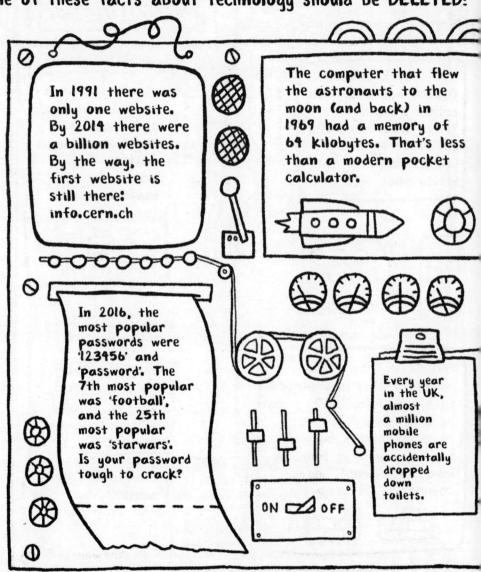

In 1991 there was only one website. By 2014 there were a billion websites. By the way, the first website is still there: info.cern.ch

The computer that flew the astronauts to the moon (and back) in 1969 had a memory of 64 kilobytes. That's less than a modern pocket calculator.

In 2016, the most popular passwords were '123456' and 'password'. The 7th most popular was 'football', and the 25th most popular was 'starwars'. Is your password tough to crack?

Every year in the UK, almost a million mobile phones are accidentally dropped down toilets.

ON OFF

WHICH FACT IS AN ERROR?
∗/?!!//@∗#

The search engine Google was originally called 'Backrub'. Yahoo was originally called 'Jerry and David's Guide to the World Wide Web'.

The first mobile phones had to be charged for 10 hours. The battery then lasted for 30 minutes.

The smallest robots in the world are called nanobots. They can be around 100 nanometres in length – so roughly one thousand times smaller than this full stop ⟹.

Bill Gates, the founder of Microsoft, is obsessed with Lego. In 2005, he surprised a meeting of shareholders by showing up in a pair of large blue shoes, made completely of Lego.

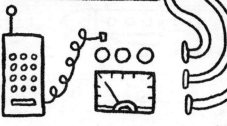

Answer

To find out the answer, we're going to use CALCULATOR LANGUAGE — the letters that numbers become if you turn your calculator UPSIDE DOWN, e.g. 1 = I, 2 = Z, 3 = E, 4 = H and so on...

First, do the sums below on a calculator, then turn the answer upside down and write what you see.

Write the answer UPSIDE DOWN here.

The fact about

_ _ _ _
3859 × 2

Gates and his

_ _ _ _   _ _ _ _ _
1.911 ÷ 3   40700 + 12345

is a

_ _ _   _ _ _ !
428.729 - 111.111

This is two words — separated by a decimal point.

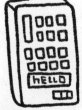

Other words you can spell upside down on a calculator include 'bellies', 'eggshells', 'oboe' and 'sleigh'. Can you think of any others?

Still stuck? Turn to page 157 for the answer.

SPEW OR FALSE?

Sick of all the lies? Spot the fake vomit fact!

In 2002, scientists found a patch of fossilised dinosaur sick in Peterborough, UK. It was 160 million years old.

I told you that stegosaurus was off.

Over half of astronauts throw up when they first arrive in zero gravity. They use a special 'barf bag' or the sick floats into their face.

Uh-oh...

Lazzaro Spallanzani lived in the 18th century and was a pretty strange scientist. In one experiment, he ate some food, puked it up, ate the sick, threw THAT up and then ate the sicked-up sick!

During banquets, ancient Romans had special rooms called vomitoriums where they threw up in between courses to make space for more food.

The Dive Coaster in Guangzhou, China, is supposed to be the world's most vomit-inducing roller coaster. On leaving the ride, customers are given a choice of a vomit bag or a vomit bin.

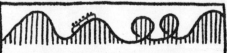

Answer over here ⟶

RIDICULOUS RULES

Seven of these laws are REAL. Which one is too ludicrous to be true?

In Florida, USA, you're not allowed to fart in a public place after 6pm on Thursdays.

In West Virginia, USA, it's against the law to go hunting with a ferret.

In Wisconsin, USA, it's illegal to sell stinky cheese.

It is illegal for aliens to land their UFOs in Châteauneuf-du-Pape, France.

ANSWER
Ancient Romans did not have special rooms where they threw up. 'Vomitorium' meant the entrance or exit of a theatre or stadium.

Draw someone breaking the FAKE law here. (Don't worry, it's a fake law, they won't get into trouble!)

In Melbourne, Australia, you're not allowed to hoover after 10pm.

In Ulaanbaatar, Mongolia, you're not allowed to put a false beard on a panda.

In Texas, USA, it's illegal to sell your own eyeballs.

In Granville, France, you're not allowed to take an elephant to the beach.

Which law is a lie? Answer over here

To help us spot the false law, we've recruited Lieutenant Lou Tennant to help us. Like most police officers, she uses something called the **NATO** phonetic alphabet to send important messages. There's a dictionary over there to help you decode her words.

TANGO HOTEL ECHO

FOXTROT ALPHA CHARLIE TANGO

ALPHA BRAVO OSCAR UNIFORM TANGO

PAPA ALPHA NOVEMBER DELTA ALPHA SIERRA

ALPHA NOVEMBER DELTA

FOXTROT ALPHA LIMA SIERRA ECHO

BRAVO ECHO ALPHA ROMEO DELTA SIERRA

INDIA SIERRA

FOXTROT ALPHA KILO ECHO

POLICE NOTICEBOARD

A = Alpha	N = November
B = Bravo	O = Oscar
C = Charlie	P = Papa
D = Delta	Q = Quebec
E = Echo	R = Romeo
F = Foxtrot	S = Sierra
G = Golf	T = Tango
H = Hotel	U = Uniform
I = India	V = Victor
J = Juliett	W = Whiskey
K = Kilo	X = X-ray
L = Lima	Y = Yankee
M = Mike	Z = Zulu

WANTED

Evil Ninja
£5 reward

JAKE'S CAKES

Free Doughnut Voucher

HAVE YOU SEEN THIS DOG?

ANSWERS TO THE NAME OF 'BUTCH'. IF FOUND, PLEASE CONTACT PC JOE KING.

POLICE CHARITY RAFFLE

PRIZES

1. New handcuffs
2. Fluorescent jacket
3. Whistle with very loud peep

That's Lou ⟶

75

DUBIOUS DINNERS

Iona Bakpak is on a mission to travel to every country and taste the local food. But there's a FAKE photo in her scrapbook. Which food is fiction?

This is me eating fried tarantulas. It's a popular snack in Cambodia. Talk about food with bite!

In Mexico, I tried ants' eggs. They were eggs-cellent!

GRUB'S UP! In China, my friends BUGGED me to try a centipede. So I did.

I'm a sucker for octopus. In Korea, I ordered a LIVE one. It's a local speciality.

In Canada, I had a jellied moose's nose. Not to be sniffed at!

In Albania, I tried grilled mole.

I had roasted rat in Vietnam, wrapped in banana leaves. Guess that's one way to get rid of them!

In India, cow's urine can be more expensive than milk. It's meant to have special healing properties.

This meal just flew by! It was boiled dragonflies, served in coconut milk. It's a speciality in Indonesia.

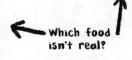
Which food isn't real?

Answer over here

In her travels, Iona's learnt LOADS of foreign words. So she's put the answer in lots of different languages. See if you can figure it out.

Je n'ai pas mangé une taupe et je ne suis jamais allée en Albanie.

Ich habe noch nie einen Maulwurf gegessen und war noch nie in Albanian.

No he comido un topo. Y nunca he estado en Albania.

Non ho mangiato una talpa. E non sono mai andata in Albania.

Я никогда не ела кротов. И я никогда не бывала в Албании.

If you haven't learnt any foreign languages yet, turn to page 157 for the answer.

BRILLIANT BANANAS

Answer below

Four of these facts are correct. One is... bananas. Can you pick it out?

1 Banana plants 'walk'. Their roots grow horizontally (rather than down), so sometimes the main stem shifts sideways in the soil – up to 40 centimetres in some cases. This makes it look like it's 'walking'. ARGH!

2 Don't throw that peel away! Apparently it's edible. It's bitter, tough and chewy – but edible.

3 Bananas can be red too. The fruit inside is pink rather than cream-coloured.

4 Bananas float in water. So do apples and pears, but grapes sink.

5 During the Second World War, the first bananas appeared in the UK – but they were sold on the black market (that is, illegally).

ANSWER
Fact 5 is fiction. In 1999, archaeologists found a banana skin in a Tudor rubbish tip. They believe the UK's first banana arrived in the mid-1800s, almost 600 years ago!

79

BAD BACTERIA

Here is a page of MICROSCOPIC bacteria. But which fact is a fib? There's a TINY answer at the bottom of the page – but you might need a magnifying glass to read it.

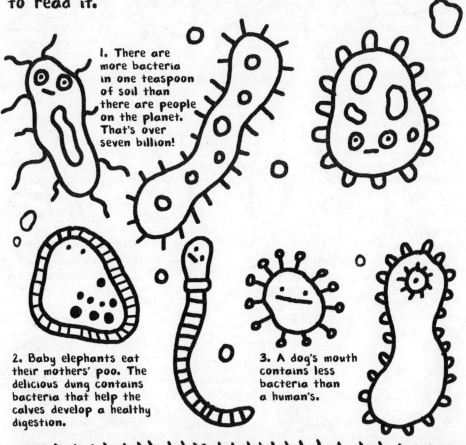

1. There are more bacteria in one teaspoon of soil than there are people on the planet. That's over seven billion!

2. Baby elephants eat their mothers' poo. The delicious dung contains bacteria that help the calves develop a healthy digestion.

3. A dog's mouth contains less bacteria than a human's.

Colour in the bacteria with the WEIRDEST and GROSSEST combinations of colours you can think of.

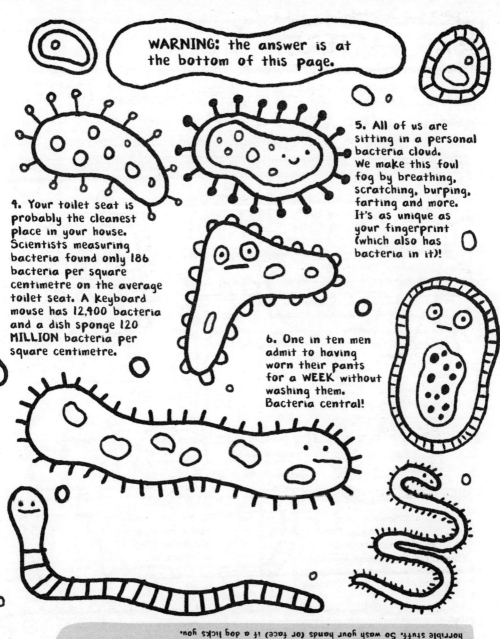

WARNING: the answer is at the bottom of this page.

4. Your toilet seat is probably the cleanest place in your house. Scientists measuring bacteria found only 186 bacteria per square centimetre on the average toilet seat. A keyboard mouse has 12,900 bacteria and a dish sponge 120 MILLION bacteria per square centimetre.

5. All of us are sitting in a personal bacteria cloud. We make this foul fog by breathing, scratching, burping, farting and more. It's as unique as your fingerprint (which also has bacteria in it)!

6. One in ten men admit to having worn their pants for a WEEK without washing them. Bacteria central!

ANSWER

Fact 3 is false! People who let their dogs lick their faces ALWAYS say this. But dogs' mouths aren't much cleaner than ours! They sniff, lick and sometimes eat all kinds of horrible stuff. So wash your hands (or face) if a dog licks you.

THE WRITING'S ON THE WALL

The Great Wall of China is the longest man-made structure that has ever been built. But one of these stories has no foundation in fact... which one?

1. The wall was started in around 770 BC. Work continued on it for the next 2,000 years.

Only 1,999 years to go!

2. Building the wall was made easier by a great Chinese invention – the wheelbarrow!

This rocks!

And rolls!

3. Other ancient Chinese inventions may also have helped with wall-building.

the compass (206 BC)

gunpowder (9th century)

paper (100 BC)

4. It's built on top of dead people! An estimated 400,000 people died while building the wall and many were buried right next to it.

RIP   RIP

5. Many of the bricks are held together by sticky rice.

The rice has done such a good job of gluing the bricks together that weeds still can't grow in the gaps.

6. The wall was a huge achievement. It remains the longest man-made structure on Earth.

7. It's 21,196 kilometres long. That's about three times longer than the continent of Africa.

8. It's visible from the moon with the naked eye.

I see the neighbours have had the builders in.

9. It's a major tourist attraction. In 2014, an estimated 16 million people visited it in ONE WEEK.

Disneyland Paris 14.8 million people in 2015

Great Wall of China 16 million people in ONE week

10. Some people visit ALL of it. In 1984, Dong Yaohui started to walk its entire length.

He finished almost a year and a half later.

11. But did the wall actually work? Er... not exactly. The Xiongnu overran it in 200 BC because it was too long to guard.

deserted

12. The Mongols also got past it in the 13th century because it had gaps in.

This great wall ain't so great.

So which of these facts has holes in it too?

The Chinese lanterns below contain every number from 1 to 12. Except for one. And THAT'S the bad fact. Can you work out which number is missing?

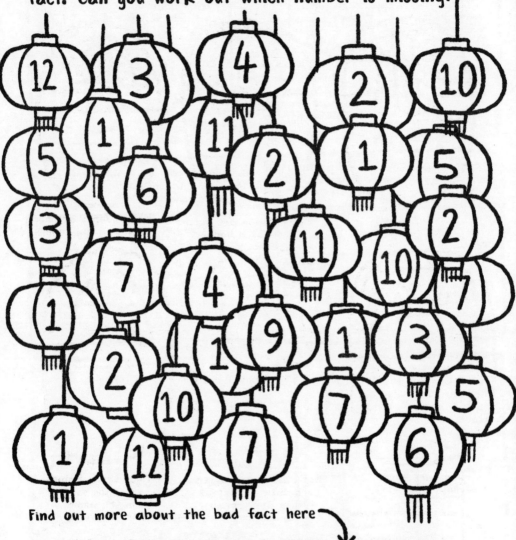

Find out more about the bad fact here

The Great Wall is definitely not visible from the moon. You can't even see it from the International Space Station (which is in low orbit). It's far too narrow!

BABY TALK

Which of these facts about baby animals is nonsense?

Baby camels have no humps.

Baby rhinos are born without a horn.

Baby cobras are born without any venom.

Dogs are born without any teeth.

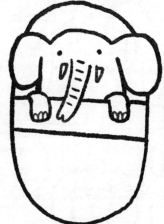
Baby elephants often suck their trunks as if they were thumbs.

Tiger shark babies eat each other in the womb.

ANSWER
The cobra fact isn't true. Baby snakes are born with all their venom and can bite you – and kill you – as soon as they are born.

85

SILLY SMUGGLERS

Smugglers are people who bring objects into countries illegally. This can involve bizarre - and sometimes cruel - behaviour. Can you spot the FAKE smuggler's tale?

1. In Stockholm, Sweden, one woman was stopped by customs officials when she kept scratching her shirt. She had **75 live snakes** hidden in her bra.

2. In Los Angeles, USA, Robert Cusack was arrested when four birds of paradise flew out of his suitcase. He also had two slow lorises in his underpants.

3. In Los Angeles, USA, one smuggler was caught trying to smuggle 240 fish through customs. He had four hard-sided suitcases full of nothing but water and fish!

4. In 2014, one passenger tried to sneak through customs in Birmingham, UK, with a huge squash (a type of vegetable). It was over a metre long and weighed over 25 kilograms.

Sniffer dogs are used in airports to sniff out anything suspicious in people's luggage. Draw a sniffer dog, or just its pawprint, on the FAKE FACT.

5. In 2011, a man arrived in Bangkok, Thailand, with 451 turtles and seven crocodiles hidden in his suitcases.

6. In 2002, a 17-year-old tourist flew from Dubai, UAE, to Manchester, UK, with a chameleon on her head, claiming that it was a hat. However, passengers on the plane spotted it moving.

Answer →

7. In 2010, officials at Miami airport, USA, found a mummy's sarcophagus in a shipment from Spain. The sarcophagus had been stolen from Egypt over 125 years earlier.

8. In Sydney, Australia, customs officials opened a suitcase to find a stuffed koala dressed as Marilyn Monroe.

Travellers, sailors and lifeguards have used semaphore for over 200 years. It involves holding two coloured flags in different directions. The answer to this smuggling quiz is in seriously secret semaphore.

(There's a code book over there if you get stuck.)

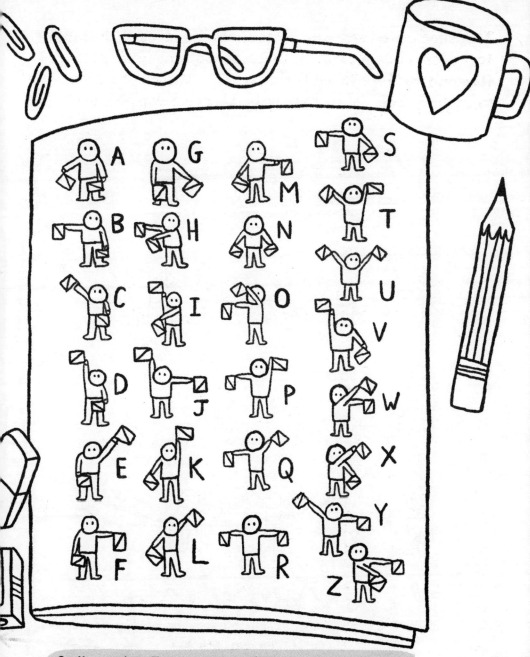

Still stuck? Turn to page 158 for the answer.

TOILET TALES

Which of these toilet facts is a rotten stinking lie?

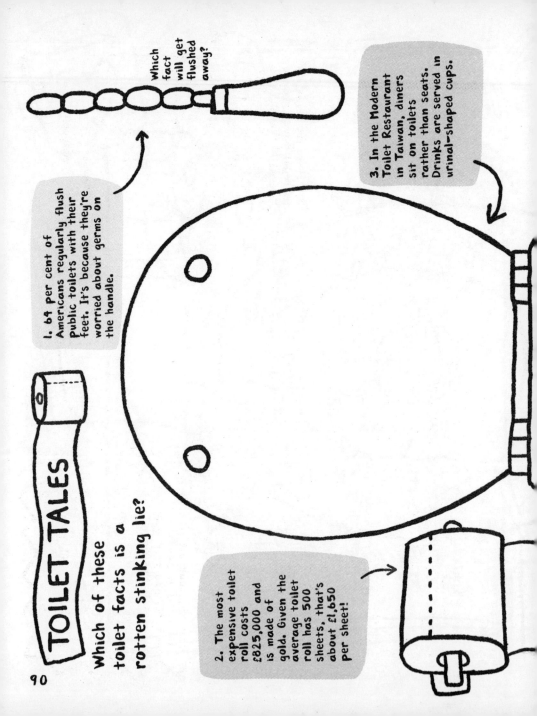

Which fact will get flushed away?

1. 64 per cent of Americans regularly flush public toilets with their feet. It's because they're worried about germs on the handle.

2. The most expensive toilet roll costs £825,000 and is made of gold. Given the average toilet roll has 500 sheets, that's about £1,650 per sheet!

3. In the Modern Toilet Restaurant in Taiwan, diners sit on toilets rather than seats. Drinks are served in urinal-shaped cups.

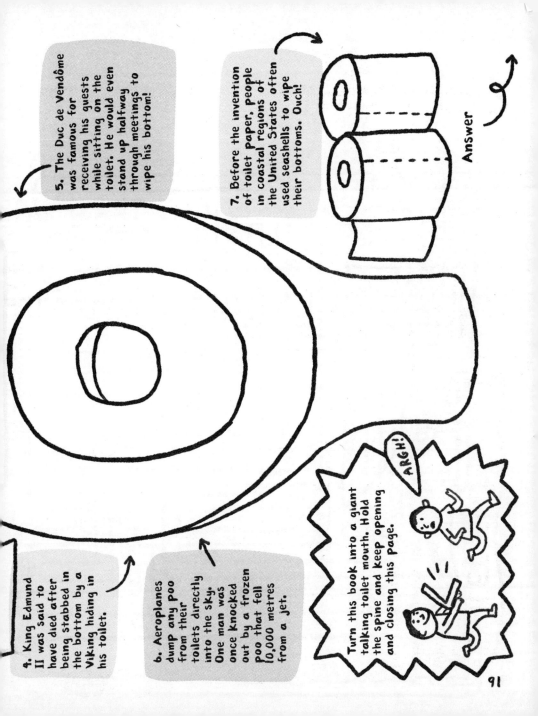

5. The Duc de Vendôme was famous for receiving his guests while sitting on the toilet. He would even stand up halfway through meetings to wipe his bottom!

7. Before the invention of toilet paper, people in coastal regions of the United States often used seashells to wipe their bottoms. Ouch!

Answer

4. King Edmund II was said to have died after being stabbed in the bottom by a Viking hiding in his toilet.

6. Aeroplanes dump any poo from their toilets directly into the sky. One man was once knocked out by a frozen poo that fell 10,000 metres from a jet.

Turn this book into a giant talking toilet mouth. Hold the spine and keep opening and closing this page.

ARGH!

91

Here are seven toilets representing the seven facts on the last page. The 'good fact' toilets lead to the SEWER OF TRUTH. The 'bad fact' toilet will be blocked. (Turn to page 158 for help!)

SEWER OF TRUTH

FEARSOME PHOBIAS

All of these are genuine names for particular phobias. Except for one...

COULROPHOBIA
fear of clowns

SOSSOPHOBIA
fear of sausages

POGONOPHOBIA
fear of beards

OMPHALOPHOBIA
fear of belly buttons

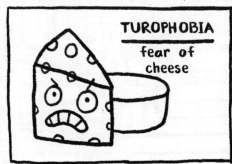

TUROPHOBIA
fear of cheese

PANPHOBIA
fear of everything

POINT
and
SCREAM
at the
bad
fact.

ANSWER As far as we know, there is no such thing as a fear of sausages.

DRAMATIC DESERTS

These desert facts may look like a mirage. But they're **all TRUE. Except one.**

A desert is anywhere with less than 25 centimetres of rain a year. This means the biggest desert on the planet is Antarctica!

Desert animals such as the fennec fox and the dorcas gazelle can survive without ever drinking water. They get all the fluid they need from the food they eat.

In some parts of the Atacama desert in Chile, it has not rained for over 400 years.

Every year, residents of Oatman, Arizona, USA, stage a competition in which they try to fry eggs on the pavement. They can use magnifying glasses and mirrors to help them, but no electricity.

Marathon runner Mauri Prosperi was lost in the Sahara desert for 10 days. He ate raw lizards and drank wee and bat's blood to survive.

The Sahara desert is 99 per cent sand and only 1 per cent other material.

UGH

More people drown in deserts than die of thirst. This is because mountain rain can pour down into valleys, causing flash floods.

Follow the tracks for the answer!

PANT ATTACK!

Answer down there

There are seven facts about pants on this page. But one of them is... er... PANTS.

King Tutankhamun was buried with 145 spare pairs of pants – for use in the afterlife.

During the Second World War, six British airmen crash-landed in the Atlantic Ocean and survived for 11 days at sea by catching fish with their underpants.

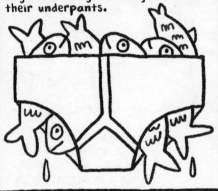

The largest ever pair of pants was 20 metres long. It was made for a charity event in 2010.

Largest pants ever 20 m

Diplodocus 21 m

The Great Norwegian Pant War broke out in 1326, when the King of Norway ordered all his subjects to wear new, hygienic French breeches. His subjects refused, burning the 'official' pants in huge bonfires.

I guess you could call them hot pants.

In 2014, 314 people in Warwick, UK, managed to squeeze into a single pair of underpants – the most ever.

This is pant-tastic!

This is a stitch-up!

Some children in the UK used to be covered in goose fat and sewn into their winter underclothes. They'd keep their 'winter pants' on until spring!

In 1930, exploding pants brought chaos to New Zealand. It was caused by a type of weedkiller that farmers were spraying on their crops. The weedkiller reacted with the cotton in the farmers' trousers and led to fiery eruptions.

Pants on fire!

ANSWER The Great Norwegian Pant War isn't real!

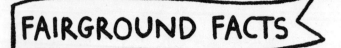

FAIRGROUND FACTS

Fairs are fantastic. But which of these facts is (loop the) loopy?

1. Richard Rodriquez rode the roller coasters at Blackpool Pleasure Beach, in the UK, ALL DAY for 112 consecutive days, stopping only when the park was closed. This is a world record!

2. The Formula Rossa roller coaster in the UAE goes from 0 km/h to 240 kilometres an hour in FIVE SECONDS.

3. In 2010, a doctor in Blackpool spent £1,200 trying to win a fluffy rabbit on a hoopla stall.

4. The world record for the highest number of clowns to climb out of a clown car is 117.

5. The leotard is named after Jules Leotard, a famous French trapeze artist, who wore one during his shows.

6. It would take around 2,043 helium balloons to lift the average nine-year-old boy off the ground. (If you want to work out how many you'd need to fly, then a helium balloon can lift around 14 grams. So divide your weight in GRAMS by 14!)

Answer on the next page.

7. Candy floss has only one ingredient – sugar (plus, sometimes, food colouring). It was invented by a dentist.

ANSWER
The Sahara desert is not 99 per cent sand. It's more like 30 per cent sand and 70 per cent gravel, rocks and other stuff. Remember: being a desert is based on the amount of rainfall, not the amount of sand!

Roll up! Roll up! And welcome to the fairground...

ANSWER PAGE.

To make things more fun, I'm going to give you a

MAGNIFICENT and MAGICAL

MEMORY TEST.

So, without turning back and checking, can you remember:

How many loops were in the looping roller coaster?

How many coconuts in the coconut shy?

How many flags were on the big top?

Your answers should all be the same - and that's the number of the

BAD FACT.

For those with bad memories (like me), the answer is also upside-down here:

ANSWER
There's no way 117 clowns could fit into a clown car! Clown cars aren't a trick - the clowns actually have to squeeze in! The record for the most people ever squeezed into a Mini is 27, so that gives you an idea of the maximum number of clowns per clown car.

NIFTY NINJAS

Which of these ninja facts is nonsense?

PSST! Ninjas sent secret messages using coloured grains of rice.

Women could be ninjas: their weapons included 'cat claws' (sharp knives that were often dipped in poison) and special folding fans which could fend off darts and also be thrown as a weapon.

Ninjas always wore jet-black uniforms so they were invisible at night.

Ninjas often carried a box with a cricket inside. The chirping of the cricket would mask their footsteps (and any accidental snapped twigs) and make people think that it was just an ordinary summer night...

Ninjas didn't usually assassinate people. They tended to be sent on spying missions, working undercover and collecting information.

Answer over here

OCTOPUS AWESOMENESS

Octopuses are amazing. But which of these seven facts is suspect? Scribble on the SNEAKY sign!

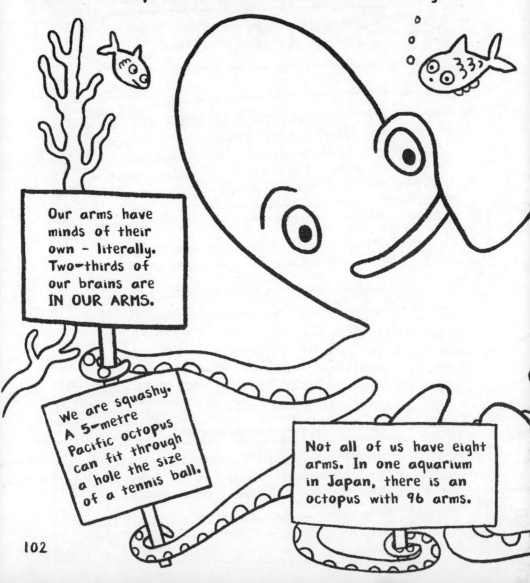

Our arms have minds of their own – literally. Two-thirds of our brains are IN OUR ARMS.

We are squashy. A 5-metre Pacific octopus can fit through a hole the size of a tennis ball.

Not all of us have eight arms. In one aquarium in Japan, there is an octopus with 96 arms.

We mate for life and live in large family groups called 'spargles'.

We squirt ink when we are threatened. This ink can be red, brown or black. (Our blood is blue though.)

Some of us have been spotted walking onto dry land and eating seagulls.

We are ingenious. We can solve mazes, lift latches and open child-proof medicine bottles. Because of this, we often stage dramatic escapes from aquariums!

Follow this arm for the answer

NINJA ANSWER
The idea that ninjas wore black all the time is a myth. They were spies, so often they wore regular clothes to help them blend in.

RANDOM RECORDS

Don't try any of these yourself!

There have been some wonderfully WEIRD world records. But which one is too random to be real? Draw a gold star on the genuine records.

Ilker Yilmaz holds the record for squirting milk out of his eye. In 2008, he managed to eye-shoot milk for 2 metres and 79.5 centimetres.

In 2002, Lars Clausen crossed the USA twice, covering almost 15,000 kilometres. And he did ALL of it on a UNICYCLE.

ANSWER
Octopuses don't mate for life. In fact, female octopuses often strangle the males after mating (and sometimes eat them). And they don't live in groups, they live alone. When octopuses meet, they tend to fight.

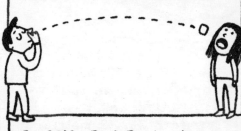

In 2012, Paul Prado shot a marshmallow 5.46 metres out of his nostril, straight into the mouth of catcher Sophia Rojas.

This is a rattling good stunt!

Jackie Bibby put seven rattlesnakes down his trousers for 15 minutes in 2014. He survived unbitten.

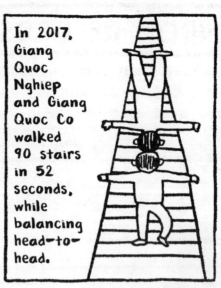

In 2017, Giang Quoc Nghiep and Giang Quoc Co walked 90 stairs in 52 seconds, while balancing head-to-head.

Answer this way

Talk about a face lift!

In 2008, Georges Christen picked up an 11.8-kilogram table with a 50-kilogram woman sitting on it IN HIS MOUTH and then carried it for 12 metres.

I'm going to skip to the end!

Ashrita Furman has the Guinness World Record for the most Guinness World Records. He currently holds almost 200, including highest mountain climbed on stilts and most jumps on an underwater skipping rope (in one hour).

ANSWER
Jackie Bibby didn't put seven rattlesnakes down his trousers. But he DOES hold the world record for sitting in a bath with the most snakes (195).

WONDERFUL WORDS

SCRIBBLE OUT THE FAKE FACT!

Which of these facts about words and language is goobledegook?

1. The average British person says 'sorry' 1.9 million times in their lifetime.

2. You can write out every number until you reach one billion without ever using the letter 'b'.

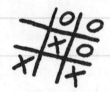

3. Over 850 different languages are spoken in Papua New Guinea. But only 7.3 million people live there - fewer than in London or New York.

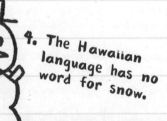

4. The Hawaiian language has no word for snow.

5. 'Iksuarpok' is an Inuit word which is hard to translate. It means 'constantly getting up to check if the friend you're expecting has arrived yet'.

Which fact is a fib?

6. Another hard-to-translate word is 'schadenfreude' (pronounced 'shah-den-froy-der'). It's a German word that means 'laughing when somebody else messes up'. Like when your friend misses a penalty kick or your sister drops toast (face down) on her school uniform. Useful, eh?

7. Only two English words end with 'gry' – angry and hungry. 'Hangry' is a word invented in 2005 to mean 'feeling angry because you're feeling hungry'.

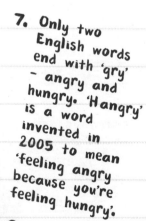

8. Emojis are the world's fastest growing language.

Answer this way →

ACROSS

1. How many sides does a square have? (4)

2. Complete the song title from 'The Lion King': 'I Just ____ Wait To Be King'. (4)

6. A word meaning 'since' or 'for this reason'. For example: 'I like crisps _____ they taste fantastic'. (7)

8. Opposite of isn't. Rhymes with quiz! (2)

9. Complete the name of the fairy tale: '____ White and the Seven Dwarves.' (4)

11. Opposite of against. Sounds like ONE ACROSS but spelt differently. (3)

DOWN

1. Complete the book title: 'Splat the Fake ____!' (4)

3. What every fact should be. (4)

4. What's the missing word? ___ Lion, ___ Witch and ___ Wardrobe. (3)

5. A ham and pineapple pizza is commonly known as a _____. (8)

6. What word is missing from this Shakespeare quote? 'To __ or not to __, that is the question.' (2)

10. The puzzle you're doing at the moment is called a cross____. (4)

If you get stuck, turn to page 158.

CRAZY CRISPS

Eight of these are ACTUAL crisp flavours that have appeared in at least ONE country. One is too crackers to be a crisp! Scribble out the bad fact!

OCTOPUS
Called 'Tako chips', they're big in Japan

COFFEE
Sold in the USA since 2014

A fake flavour?

MILK CHOCOLATE
Sold in the USA since 2013

KRUNCHY CRISPS

CHICKEN AND PEPSI
Popular in China since 2012

PESKY PIRATES

There are a lot of peculiar pirate yarns. But which one of these should be THROWN OVERBOARD? Draw a cannonball heading for the FAKE fact.

1. Most pirate crews had a flag. The most famous was the 'Jolly Roger'. But other flags were used to send signals. For example, a blood red flag meant 'No life will be spared'.

2. Pirates were tough on anyone who crossed them. The most common punishment was walking the plank.

3. Famous pirate Olivier Levasseur captured a Portuguese treasure ship. When the loot was divided, each member of his crew received at least 50,000 guineas (over £4 million in today's money) and 42 diamonds each.

4. Pirates often had more than one boat. Chinese pirate Madame Ching Shih had 1,800 ships under her command and 80,000 sailors.

5. After disguising herself as a man, Anne Bonny (the 'Pirate Queen') ran away to sea with her lover 'Calico' Jack Rackham in around 1718. When the Navy attacked Jack's ship, Anne and her friend Mary Read were the only ones who put up a fight!

6. Earrings meant a lot to pirates. They were often earned as a reward for especially dangerous voyages. If a pirate died, his earrings would pay for the cost of his funeral.

7. In the 18th century, most merchant ships were terrified of pirates. If they had no weapons, some would paint PRETEND cannons on the sides of their ships to put off attackers.

Which fact is false? Answer over the page

Fact 2 is the BAD fact. There's only ONE recorded case of a pirate making anyone walk the plank. In fact, there are lots of myths about pirates. Here are a few of them...

WANTED
Bad Fact

WALKING THE PLANK
Pirate punishments included being whipped and being marooned on a desert island. But almost NEVER walking the plank.

£500 REWARD
for this PIRATE MYTH

BURYING TREASURE
Pirates rarely buried their treasure. Because it was stolen, they sold or spent it – FAST.

£1,000 REWARD
for this FEARSOME FIB

Why am I a pirate?

Because you ARRR.

SAYING 'ARRR' A LOT
Pirates only talk like this in films. Real pirates came from all over the world and had lots of different accents.

WANTED
PRETEND PIRATE FACT

Pieces of eight!

A PARROT ON THE SHOULDER
This was invented by Robert Louis Stevenson in the book 'Treasure Island'. (Although real pirates DID keep pets.)

HOW MUCH?

Do you know the names of really BIG numbers? One of the descriptions below is definitely not correct. But which one? Delete the error.

Answer below.
↓

1,000,000 = a million

1,000,000,000 = a billion

1,000,000,000,000 = a trillion

1,000,000,000,000,000 = a quadrillion

1,000,000,000,000,000,000 = a quintillion

1,000,000,000,000,000,000,000 = a zillion

ANSWER There is no such number as a zillion (or a gazillion or a bazillion). The last number here is a SEXTILLION (1 and 21 zeroes).

115

ODD JOBS

Butcher, baker, candlestick maker. People have all KINDS of jobs. Here are seven of the strangest. And ONE fake...

VIDEO GAME PLAYER
In South Korea, this is an actual job. Top players have their games shown on TV and earn huge amounts of money. People ask them for selfies and autographs.

WATER SLIDE TESTER
In 2013, Tommy Lynch got a job testing hundreds of water slides for holiday company First Choice. Woo-hoo!

PROFESSIONAL APOLOGISER
Sorry, what? In Japan, you can hire an 'apolgiser' to say sorry to someone if you don't want to do it yourself.

BOTTOM WIPER
How about the WORST JOB ever? In Tudor times, the Groom of the Stool was responsible for wiping the King's bottom. And since there was no toilet paper yet, he'd have to do this with his BARE HANDS.

YOU'RE FIRED!
Draw a giant boss's finger pointing at the made-up job. FIRE the PHONEY!

DOG FOOD TASTER
All dog food has to be 'fit for human consumption' — just in case a toddler accidentally eats some. Which means that someone's job is eating dog food ALL DAY.

Breakfast Lunch Dinner

HUMAN SCARECROW
22-year-old Jamie Fox was hired as a human scarecrow in 2012 to keep partridges away from a 1.6-hectare field in Aylsham, UK.

CLOUD CARVER
These people go up into the sky in aeroplanes and carve clouds into animal shapes during music festivals. They use a special tool called a 'sky scoop'.

SLEEPER
In 2013, a hotel in Finland hired a professional sleeper. Their job was to have a snooze in all 35 of the hotel's rooms and report back on how well they slept.

Answer over here

Here is a cloud carver getting fired. That was the FAKE job. You can draw what he's about to land in if you like.

Cloud carvers aren't real, unfortunately. They were invented by a writer for grown-ups called J.G. Ballard. He was trying to think of all the cool jobs that MIGHT be possible one day. Can you imagine any other AMAZING new jobs?

In the future, I'd like to be:

SPECTACULAR SPELLING

These words are said to be some of the HARDEST to spell in the English language. So for each word, I've given you TWO spellings. Circle the right one in each option.

 If something's strange, is it:
weird or wierd

 Is a repeated pattern of beats:
a rhythm or a rythm

 If you feel confused and awkward, are you:
embarrassed or embarassed

 If something's already happened, has it:
occured or occurred

 If something needs to be done, is it:
necessery or necessary

 If someone draws something on a wall, is it:
graffiti or graffitti

 And if something's not spelled properly, is it:
misspelled or mispelled

Answer ----> 119

NASTY PLANTS

Most plants are lovely. We eat them, wear them and build houses with them. But some plants are **NOT NICE AT ALL.** Here are five of the nastiest. And one pretend plant.

The 'monkey cup' pitcher plant is one of the most fearsome meat-eating plants. Up to six metres long, it eats primarily insects, but also rodents, frogs and birds.

The gympie gympie is the most toxic of Australia's stinging trees. Just brushing past the leaves can cause pain for months – or even years. One victim, Les Moore, said he 'looked like Mr Potato Head' after being stung in the face.

You can usually spot manchineel trees because they have signs on them saying: 'Warning! Don't touch this tree'. Just one bite of the green fruit can kill you. ONE DROP of the sap can scorch your skin.

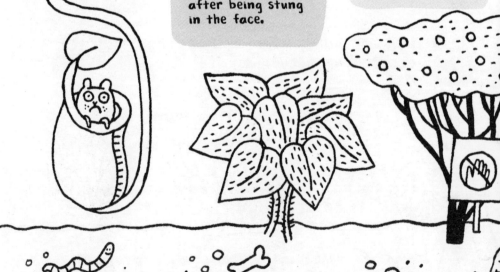

⇨ ANSWER The right spellings are: weird, rhythm, embarrassed, occurred, necessary, graffiti and misspelled.

Use weedkiller on the bad fact! Draw a bottle squirting spray next to the plant that you think is **NONSENSE**.

Answer ⟶

Eating just **HALF** a death cap mushroom can be **FATAL**. And there's no cure! One of these fiendish fungi was probably used to poison the Roman Emperor Claudius in 54 AD.

In Nicaragua, you can find the only man-eating plant in the world – the famous 'vampire vine'. Its stalks contain little suckers which digest your flesh. The only way of escaping is by rubbing it with the leaves of the tiddli-widdli bush – which usually grows nearby.

Every part of the tobacco plant is poisonous, especially the leaves. Eating just **ONE** cigarette can kill a child. And smoking cigarettes causes over five **MILLION** deaths a year.

Follow the tree roots to find the answer...

If you get stuck, turn to page 159.

BRILLIANT BRAINS

Which of these brainy brain facts is unbelievable? Draw a lightbulb on the good facts!

1. You only ever use about ten per cent of your brain.

2. The brain cannot feel pain. If you poked it with a stick, you wouldn't feel anything.

3. Many animals have no brains at all – for example, jellyfish, starfish and sea cucumbers.

4. When you're awake, your brain generates power – up to 23 watts at any given moment. That's enough to power a lightbulb.

5. Ever tried to tickle yourself? It's impossible! Your cunning brain knows the difference between YOUR hands and other people's.

6. Albert Einstein was an incredible scientist. When he died in 1955, a doctor in the hospital stole Einstein's brain and kept it in a jar in his basement for 40 years.

ANSWER Fact 1 is false. You use most of your brain most of the time. Even when you're asleep!

ROUND THE BEND

Do you know what road signs mean? For each sign, we've given you one RIGHT answer and one BAD one. Guess which is which and cross out the one that can't be true.

1. No motor vehicles
OR
Stuntman at work

Answer below

2. Man opening umbrella
OR
Roadworks

3. Pogo stick in road
OR
Staggered junction ahead

4. Massive farts likely
OR
Beware of sidewinds

5. No right turn
OR
No boomerangs

6. Traffic lights ahead
OR
Disco in progress

7. Road is still
loading. Please wait.
OR
Roundabout ahead

8. Beware: snake eating a goat
OR
Humps in road

9. Conga line just
started. Please join in!
OR
Elderly people crossing

10. Beware of cattle OR
Wind your window up! Everything
is about to smell of cowpats!

ANSWER
1. No motor vehicles, 2. Roadworks, 3. Staggered junction ahead, 4. Beware of
sidewinds, 5. No right turn, 6. Traffic lights ahead, 7. Roundabout ahead,
8. Humps in road, 9. Elderly people crossing, 10. Beware of cattle

125

PET'S CORNER

Do you have a pet? Here are seven true stories about pets. And one beastly lie!

Draw a pawprint on the BAD fact.

Answer down there

1. When the poet Lord Byron arrived in Cambridge University in 1808, he was told he couldn't keep a dog in his room. So he brought a bear instead.

2. Lynea Lattanzio has owned over 28,000 cats. Around 1,000 currently live in her five-bedroom house in California, USA. She lives in a caravan in the garden.

3. In 2011, a dog named 'Abbie Girl' surfed a 107-metre-long wave. This is a doggie world record! Abbie Girl's owner, Michael, also takes her skydiving.

4. A cat called Stubbs has been Mayor of Talkeetna, Alaska, USA, since 1997.

Too random to be real?

5. Goldfish only have three-second memories. So if you have a goldfish, there's not much point giving it a name...

7. People in Britain have some crazy pets. In 2016, there were 13 tigers, eight leopards and 10 alligators kept as pets in ordinary homes (not zoos) in the UK. Would you want a pet that could eat you?

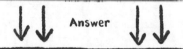

Answer

ANSWER
Fact 5 is false. Goldfish can remember things for up to three months and can even be trained to push a button to get food!

6. Pekingese dogs were first bred in China over a thousand years ago. They were known as 'sleeve dogs' because they would be carried around in the sleeves of their owners' robes. Some legends say that Chinese emperors kept one hidden in each arm to attack any assassins.

8. In 2010, a cat was rummaging in supermarket bins when she got her head stuck in a tin of cat food. Even though she couldn't see, she managed to walk through the town of Fife, UK, avoiding traffic (and dogs), before finally arriving at a local rescue centre.

SKY HIGH PRICES

How much did the Earth's most famous buildings and structures cost to build? We've put the costs below (in today's prices) and one where the cost is definitely WRONG! If you think the building fact is true, colour in the notes!

KEY

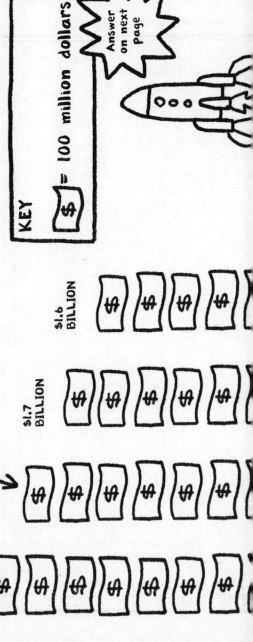

$ = 100 million dollars

Answer on next page

$1.6 BILLION

$1.7 BILLION

The price is right?

$1.8 BILLION

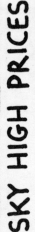

$37 BILLION
(we'd need 345 more bank notes on top of this one).

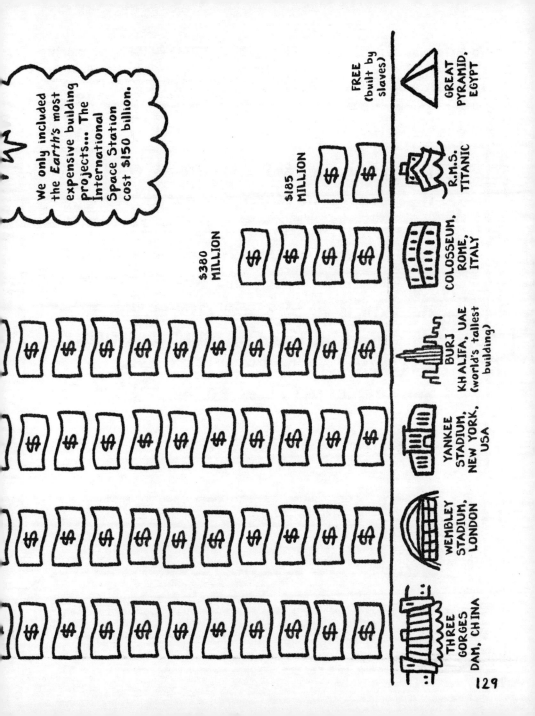

We only included the *Earth's* most expensive building projects... The International Space Station cost $150 billion.

129

To help you with the answer to SKY HIGH PRICES, a riddle has been carved on to the side of this building. It contains a vital clue about the name of the FAKE FACT

My first is in PARP and also in PONG.

My second is in SOGGY but not in SONG.

My third is in FART but not in FAT.

My fourth is in MANURE and also COWPAT.

My fifth is in MARS and also in COMET.

My sixth is in SICK and also in VOMIT.

My seventh is found in FOUND and FIDDLE

And DUNG and DRIBBLE

and UNDERPANTS and RIDDLE.

Write your answer here:

- - - - - - - - -

If you get stuck, the answer is (upside-down) here:

ANSWER
The riddle spells PYRAMID. This is the wrong fact on the chart. The Great Pyramid wasn't built for free by slaves. It was constructed by well-paid labourers. It is estimated that the pyramid would have cost almost $1 billion in today's prices.

SPREAD THE BAD FACT!

Here are five fab word puzzles. They're all designed to **TRICK** your friends into repeating BAD FACTS. Give them a try!

1. Tell your friend to repeat the word 'silk' ten times. Now ask them what cows drink? Bet they say **MILK!** But they're **WRONG**. Cows drink water.

2. Spell 'most'. Spell 'post'. Now spell 'host'. What do you put in a toaster? Did you think **TOAST?** No! It's **BREAD!** See if your friends fall for it.

3. If a red house is made from red bricks, and a blue house is made from blue bricks, and a yellow house is made from yellow bricks, what is a greenhouse made from? **NO** – not green bricks! A greenhouse is made from glass.

4. Which one is correct? 'Penguins is great at flying' or 'Penguins are great at flying'. **NEITHER!** Penguins can't fly!

5. How many months have 28 days? Did you think: 'One – February?' The right answer is – **ALL** months have 28 days in them!

How many **WRONG** facts did you get your friends to repeat?

COLD HARD FACTS

Here are five facts about frozen creatures.
Can you see through the fake story?

1. Every year, wood frogs in Alaska are frozen for seven months. Most of the water in their bodies turns to ice and their hearts stop beating. In the spring, they thaw out and hop off!

2. Tardigrades or 'water bears' can survive almost anything. In 2016, a water bear was defrosted after being frozen solid for 30 years. It came back to life and later laid 19 eggs.

3. In 2011, Wim Hof immersed himself in ice for 1 HOUR and 52 MINUTES – the longest time ever. He has also climbed 6.7 kilometres up Mount Everest wearing only shorts.

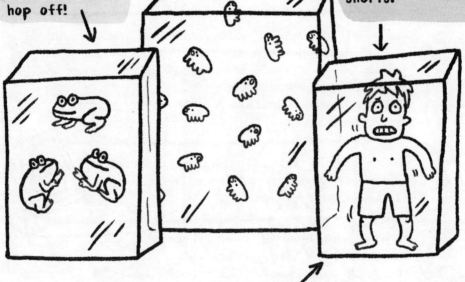

A transparent lie?

132

Draw a harpoon sticking out of the BAD iceblock fact.

4. In 2012, a British artist exhibited a giant toilet brush frozen in a block of ice in a famous galley in London. He called it 'What is Art good for?'

5. In 1991, scientists discovered the body of a Neolithic hunter preserved in a glacier in the Alps. They called the man Ötzi. He'd died about 5,000 years before and an arrow wound in his shoulder suggests it was MURDER!

6. In 2013, explorers in Antarctica found a box of black-and-white photographs in a block of ice. These images were from a 1914 expedition by Ernest Shackleton - one of the most famous explorers ever!

Answer

COLD HARD FACTS ANSWER

All of these snowmen look the same right? Wrong! One is different. And that's the number of the fake fact... If you can't spot it, turn to page 159 for the answer (and more info).

HIC!

Answer ↓

All of these are commonly suggested as cures for hiccups, except for one FAKE. Guess which one, then draw a finger **popping** the fake bubble!

Drink water through a straw while putting your fingers in your ears.

Have someone shock or surprise you.

Grab your nose, take a deep breath and hold the breath for ten seconds.

Hop 15 times on one leg, then 15 times on the other.

ANSWER
Hopping has never been seen as a traditional cure for hiccups. Though some people say that doing some quick exercises (like sit-ups) can help to get rid of them, by altering your breathing pattern.

BONUS FACT: Nobody knows why we get hiccups. But nearly all mammals DO get them!

PORTMANTEAU WORDS

A portmanteau word is one that squashes together two words to create a completely new one.

Example of a portmanteau word:
'frenemy' = friend + enemy.
E.g. 'Sometimes Bob and I get along and sometimes we really don't. We're frenemies!'

Here are **FIVE** portmanteau words and **TWO** definitions for each. Which is **GENUINE** and which is gibberish? Draw a ginormous (gigantic + enormous) tick on the right answers!

No word of a lie?

  1. Is brunch...

breakfast + lunch
E.g. 'It's 11 o'clock. Let's grab some brunch.'

OR

bang + crunch
E.g. 'I fell off my bike and hit the ground with a loud BRUNCH.'

2. Is guesstimate...

guess + estimate.
E.g. 'A new bike costs about £300. Actually, that's just a guesstimate.'

OR

quest + mate
E.g. 'I've got a guesstimate staying at the moment. She's called Susie.'

Circle your choice

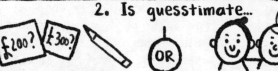

3. Is transistor...

 OR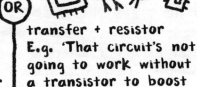

translator + sister
E.g. 'My sister's 14. She just grunts, I need some kind of transistor to understand her.'

transfer + resistor
E.g. 'That circuit's not going to work without a transistor to boost the current.'

Can't be correct? ←

4. Is chillax...

 OR

chill out + relax
E.g. 'I just want to stay in, watch a film on TV and chillax.'

chilli + earwax
E.g. 'In the Middle Ages, one cure for the flu was chilli mixed with earwax – a chillax.'

5. Is smog...

OR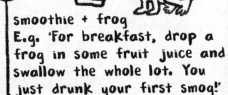

smoke + fog
E.g. 'I could hardly see outside because of the thick smog.'

smoothie + frog
E.g. 'For breakfast, drop a frog in some fruit juice and swallow the whole lot. You just drunk your first smog!'

Answers here

ANSWERS 1. Brunch = breakfast + lunch, 2. Guesstimate = guess + estimate, 3. Transistor = transfer + resistor, 4. Chillax = chill out + relax, 5. Smog = smoke + fog

TREMENDOUS TREEHOUSES

Which of these treehouse facts is solid as an oak? And which deserves the chop?

1. The Korowai people of West Papua live in huge treehouses, up to 50 metres off of the ground. They are believed to have had no contact with other humans until some scientists visited them in the 1970s.

2. Finca Bellavista is a treehouse village in Costa Rica built by Erica and Matt Hogan. Neighbours visit each other by zipwires and rope bridges.

3. The Bird's Nest treehouse is a hotel that you can stay in in Sweden. Its walls and roof are covered in huge branches so, from the outside, it looks like the nest of a gigantic bird.

Draw a WISE OWL in all the tree scenes that you think are TRUE.

Answer over → here

4. Also in Sweden, the UFO treehouse looks like a flying saucer. Guests climb up a large white ladder.

5. The world's largest treehouse is in Tennessee, USA. It has FOUR separate floors and contains a church and a basketball court. Unfortunately nobody's been allowed to live in it since 2012, because it failed a fire inspection.

6. In 1951, George Mackenzie started to build his son a treehouse. George finally finished building it in 2002, by which time his son was 58 years old.

DRAMATIC DOLPHINS

Dolphins are super-smart, carnivorous, sea-dwelling mammals. But which of these facts is a bit... fishy? Turn over for the answer!

2. Dolphins don't ever really sleep. They shut down half their brain and half their body, but keep the other half awake, just in case a predator sneaks up on them.

3. Dolphins are bald. They have a tiny bit of hair on their chin when they're born but it soon falls out. Having no hair helps them swim faster.

1. Although they live in it, dolphins can't drink saltwater. Instead, they get the water they need from the food they eat.

Treehouse fact 6 is false. George Mackenzie didn't spend 51 years building a treehouse for his son. The other facts are true though.

4. In 2004, Rob Howes and his family were swimming in New Zealand when a group of dolphins formed a circle around them. Every time Mr Howes swam away, the dolphins nudged him back into the circle. Then he realised the dolphins were protecting his family from a three-metre-long great white shark.

5. Dolphins call each other by different names – just like us. These 'names' sound (to us) like a high-pitched whistle.

6. The killer whale isn't a whale. It's a dolphin. It IS a killer though, eating seals, sea otters, octopuses, other dolphins, sharks, turtles, and baleen whales – but never humans.

7. Dolphins are solitary and like to live alone.

Although the dolphins here are performing tricks, please remember that dolphins are ALWAYS happiest in the open sea, rather than an aquarium!

Answer ⟹

Dolphins are famously intelligent. Scientists have discovered that they can do extremely TRICKY maths – including multiplication.

To celebrate this, I'm giving you the ANSWER to the dolphin page in the form of a MATHS puzzle.

1. Think of a number.
2. Double it.
3. Add 14.
4. Divide it in half.
5. Take away the number you first thought of.

Write the answer here: – – – –

Now do the puzzle again, but think of a different number.

Write the answer here: – – – –

The two answers should be THE SAME.
And THAT'S the number of the BAD dolphin fact.

For more information about the bad fact, turn to page 159.

TERRIBLE TELLY

Answer below

Here are five of the strangest **TV** shows ever made. And one I made up...

1. In 2013, a Norwegian **TV** station made a programme that showed a crackling log fireplace – for **TWELVE** hours.

2. In 2001, US show 'Whisker Wars' followed a group of people hoping to win the World's Best Beard competition.

3. One Japanese game show featured a round called 'Do Not Laugh'. If you laughed, you lost!

4. 'The Flying Nun' was a 1960s US **TV** show about a nun who could fly. There were over 80 episodes made.

5. 'Stop That Tortoise!' was a UK game show in which contestants had to escape from a locked box before a tortoise reached a pile of lettuce.

6. 'My Mother The Car' was a US comedy show in which David Crabtree's mother died and came back to life as a talking car.

Use the **THUMB** of **POWER** to switch off the made-up **TV** show. Colour the **FAKE** show in **BLACK**.

ANSWER Stop That Tortoise isn't a real show. Yet.

AT LONG LAST

There is no shortage of long things. But which of these gigantic objects is a whopping great lie...?

HOW LONG ARE WE TALKING? A kilometre (or km) is 1,000 metres. The average child takes about 12 MINUTES to walk 1 kilometre.

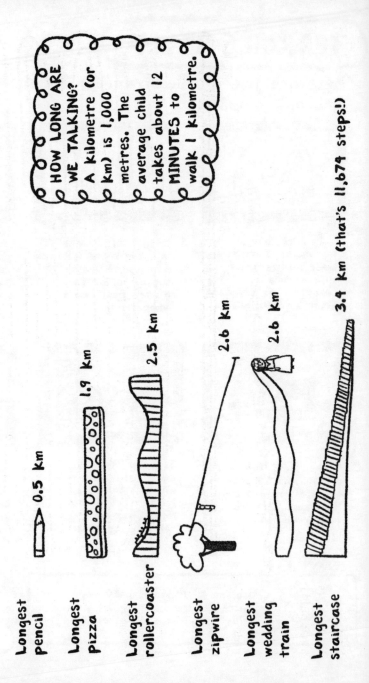

Longest pencil — 0.5 km

Longest pizza — 1.9 km

Longest rollercoaster — 2.5 km

Longest zipwire — 2.6 km

Longest wedding train — 2.6 km

Longest staircase — 3.4 km (that's 11,674 steps!)

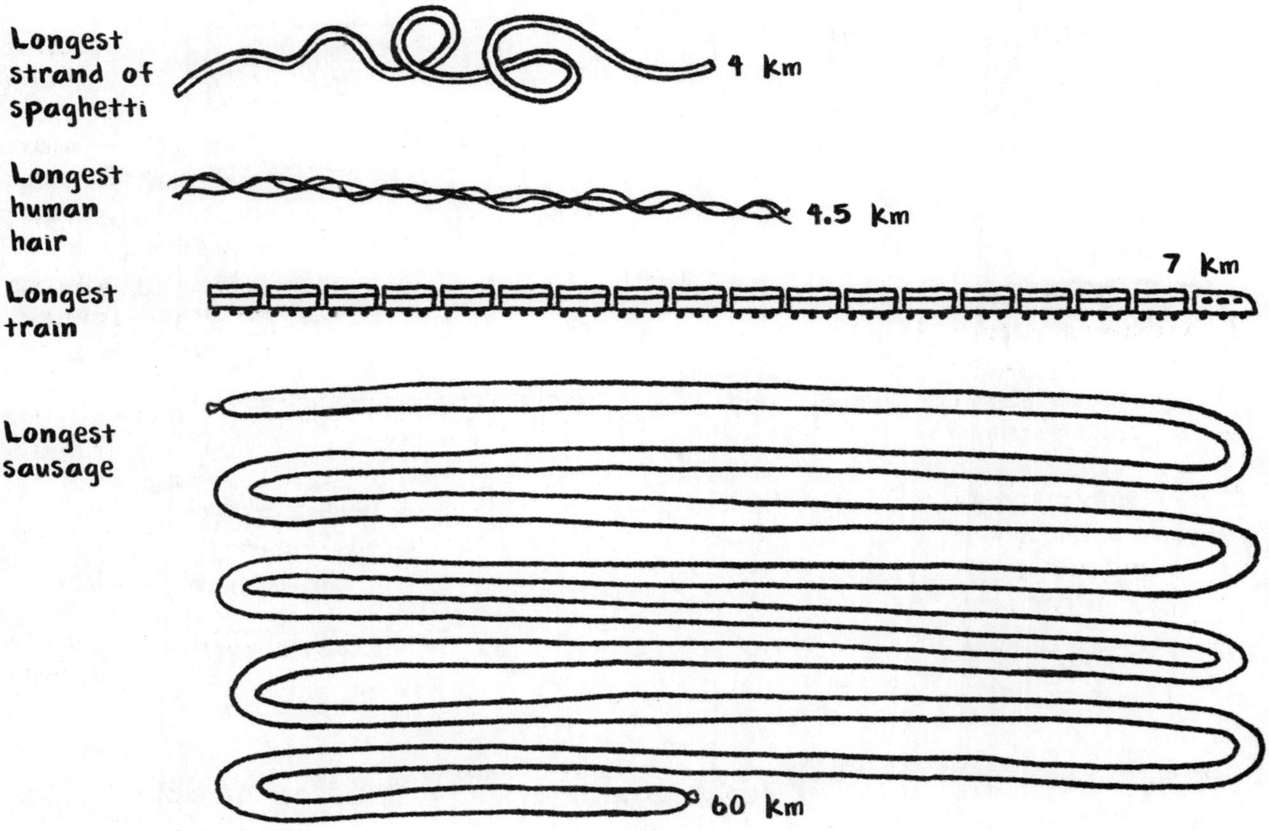

Longest
strand of
spaghetti

4 km

Longest
human
hair

4.5 km

Longest
train

7 km

Longest
sausage

60 km

Which world record is a RECORD-BREAKING fib?

Answer ↓

145

WILD WATERFALLS

Here are six waterfall facts. And one wild invention... Draw a fishing net around the BAD fact!

1. The world's highest waterfall, Angel Falls, is almost ONE KILOMETRE high. That's over 17 TIMES higher than Niagara Falls.

2. Tyler Bradt kayaked down a 57-METRE waterfall in Washington State, USA. This is the longest descent in a kayak ever.

3. Clover Peak in Ireland is the only waterfall known to flow backwards.

This has pushed me over the edge!

Answer over page

146

5. Bobby Leach survived going over Niagara Falls in a barrel in 1911. Fifteen years later, he died after slipping on an orange peel in New Zealand.

6. The biggest waterfalls on Earth are actually UNDERWATER. There's one near Greenland that drops over 3.5 kilometres.

7. Blood Falls in Antarctica is bright red because the water that feeds it is very high in iron.

4. Only about 90 per cent of fish survive the 51-metre drop over Niagara Falls. One in ten don't make it.

ANSWER to At Long Last: The longest human hair ever is only 5.6 metres. Your hair only grows 13 centimetres a year, so it could only reach 4.5 kilometres if a) if it never fell out (which it does) and b) you managed to live for 34,615 years.

INCREDIBLE ICE CREAM

There are some freaky flavours of ice cream.
But which of these is too incredible to be edible?

CHICKEN
You can find this flavour in Nagoya, Japan.

CHARCOAL
Made from charred coconut shells, you can buy this in the USA.

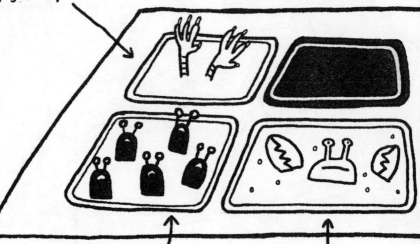

SALTED SLUG
Made by a top British restaurant, this is packed with protein!

CRAB
Another Japanese favourite, sometimes known as Kani Aisu.

ANSWER:
Fact 3 is false. Of course waterfalls can't literally flow backwards. But when winds are really strong, they can blow water UPWARDS. This has been witnessed on the Cliffs of Moher in Ireland, Kinder Downfall in England and elsewhere.

Stick your scoop in the **TRUE** flavours!

CROCODILE EGG
Made by an ice cream company in the Philippines.

CRICKET
Made by an ice cream company in Colombia, USA – the cricket's wings are used as a garnish on the top.

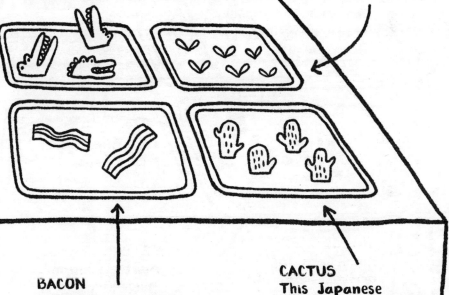

BACON
A mixture of crispy bacon and custard, this was first created by US chef David Lebovitz.

CACTUS
This Japanese speciality might leave a sharp aftertaste!

Answer!

149

ADULTS KNOW BEST?

Because this is the last fact page, things are a bit different. This is a collection of all the BAD FACTS that grown-ups tell kids. So here your job has changed. You mustn't splat the BAD fact, instead you have to find the ONLY fact that's true!

ANSWER: Salted slug ice cream is not real!

Here are the answers to the MYTHS on the last page. How did you get on?

Use this information to SPLAT bad grown-up facts whenever and wherever you find them...

CONGRATULATIONS

write your name here

_____

I hereby pronounce you a

SPECTACULAR SPLATTERER OF FICTIONAL FACTS

You are henceforth entitled to wear both

AND

ALSO the bobble hat of WISDOM

clever clogs

smarty pants

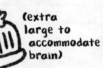

(extra large to accommodate brain)

May you always be a BEACON of HOPE for anyone who loves FACTS and THE SWORN ENEMY of any SHADY characters and SLIPPERY customers.

DR GENE YUSS
President of D.A.F.T.★

D.A.F.T.

★ The Department of Accuracy, Facts and Truth

ANSWERS

OUT OF THIS WORLD (p10-11)
The planet that's not real is Hagrid. Though he SHOULD have one named after him, shouldn't he?

EGYPTIAN FICTION? (p24-25)
The hieroglyphics read: 'Fact 4 is rubbish'. Mummies didn't wear a special pair of 'lucky' pants with their names on.

LEONARDO'S LAB (p30-31)
The secret message in the painting reads: 'Fact 4 is a lie'. Leonardo didn't design a maze that two nuns got lost in. He DID design some other cool stuff though – including a tank, a crane, a diving suit and... the first mixer tap.

BARMY BANDS (p33)
The musical notes read: 'DEAD CABBAGE CAFE'. They're a made-up band!

MIDDLE AGE MAYHEM (p40-41)

No alligators or crocodiles were ever kept in castle moats. Alligators are from the Americas and Asia, so hardly anyone in Europe would have heard of them. People HAD heard of crocodiles, because Europeans had been to North Africa, and some crocodiles were kept in royal zoos. But most people had never seen a croc, and definitely not in a moat!

BELIEVE IT OR NOT (p44-45)

The pictures in the crystal ball translate as: 'Fact 7 is not right. People in Portugal love limes'.

VOLCANO ZONE (p57)

The lava should melt Fact 4. Scientists can often predict when volcanoes are going to erupt, particularly if they know the history of when and how the volcano has erupted in the past.

SURREAL SPORTS (p60-61)

The footballers are spelling 'Big Cake Hike'. That's the made-up sport. All the others are true!